Undersea
Frontiers

Undersea Frontiers

By Gardner Soule

Exploring by Deep-Diving Submarines

Illustrated with Photographs

Rand McNally & Company

Chicago • New York • San Francisco

To Jerry Schwartz,
Anne,
Johnny,
and Kathy

Table of Contents

1 The Highway on the Bottom of the Sea   13

2 The Deepest Submarine   21

3 "It's a New World"   29

4 The Fish That Rode a Submarine   36

5 The Discovery of the Sunken Galleon   43

6 The Lifeless Depths   52

7 The "Deepstar" Monster   57

8 The Riddle of the Trench   62

9 Dive 176 for "Star II"   66

10 The Bus to the Bottom   75

11 The Mile-Deep Journey   84

12 The Travelers Beneath the Gulf Stream   91

13 The Trip to Four Miles Down   100

14 Men and Metal Under Pressure   103

15 The Black Rock   110

16 Men Under Glass Under the Sea   116

17 The Walk on the Undersea Peak   125

18 The Disappearing Seamount   131

19 "Alvin's" Dives 200-204   140

20 The Cave in the Sea Floor   150

21 The Case of the Sunken H-Bomb   162

22 The Submarines for Four Miles Down   175

23 The Dropoff into the Deep   181

24 The Bottom: "This Jules Verne World"   189

25 The Invitation to Davy Jones's Locker   201

26 The Future on the Bottom of the Sea   209

   Bibliography   223

   Index   231

List of Illustrations

Between Pages 64 and 65

Deepstar 4000 in operation
Deepstar 4000 making temperature probe
Deepstaria enigmatica before capture
Greenland shark
Rattail grenadiers and skate around bait can
Underwater man-made columns
Squid takes his own picture
Crab seen by *Aluminaut*
Manganese nodules found off Georgia
Marianas Trench as seen by *Trieste*
Brittle stars on sea floor

Between Pages 112 and 113

Deep Quest
Catamaran mother ship, *Transquest*, with *Deep Quest*
Start of world's deepest submarine dive, February 28, 1968
Frogman departs *Deep Quest* before dive
Deep Quest skipper at the helm
Alvin's mechanical arm at work
Swordfish that attacked *Alvin*
Perry *Cubmarine*, an inexpensive sub
Jacques-Yves Cousteau's *Diving Saucer*
"Sally Rand," seen off Baja, California
Star II
Star III

Between Pages 160 and 161

Asherah

Deep Diver

U. S. Navy's planned deep submergence rescue vehicle

Trieste II

First men on undersea mount with sea cucumber

Shoran recording of ocean surface and deep scattering layer

Coral niche on Seahorse Shoal

Robot sights sea serpent

Jawfish

Gorgonia off Great Swan Island

Porkfish

Ocean Systems' cachelot

Deep-sea anemones off Nantucket

Plankton as entered in *Alvin's* log

Undersea Frontiers

"You are going to visit the land of marvels."
Jules Verne, speaking of the bottom of the sea

"He goes a great Voyage, that goes to the Bottom of the Sea."
Thomas Fuller (1608–1661)

The Highway on the Bottom of the Sea

1

"Everything in oceanography," Jim Cooney said to me, "is unexpected." Cooney is in a position to know. He came to that conclusion on the bottom of the sea. He has been there, and he has looked over the bottom with his own eyes. He has done it not once, but many times.

Jim Cooney drives to work, even as you and I. There is a difference. What he drives is a deep-diving submarine. This is a brand-new type of vehicle, newer even than manned spaceships.

Cooney is one of only a handful of men who today pilot the world's first deep-diving machines. Cooney and the other pilots drive submersibles—also called research submarines or D/RV's (deep research vehicles)—that can dive far deeper than any subs before. The deep-diving pilots therefore travel to the bottom of the sea not only in shallow waters near the shore but also in deep water far at sea, to the bottom in the abyss of the ocean. They are the first men in history ever to have machines that permit them to travel back and forth regularly to and from Davy Jones's locker. The research submarines have viewports (windows) the men inside peer out of. "The main reason for their existence," Dick Usry, the pilot of one of them, *Deepstar 4000*, told me, "is their viewing ports." They also have lights to illuminate the depths. Inside a deep sub, the men cruise just above the remote, previously all but unreachable, frigid, dark, and ghostly third surface of the globe: the bottom of the sea. The other two surfaces are the surface of the land and the surface of the sea. The men in today's deepdiving submarines are the first men in history with the opportunity to become familiar, at firsthand, with the depths of the ocean and the bottom of the sea, and with the plants and the rocks and the unbelievable animals that are in the depths and on the bottom. They, like Cooney, are the first men able to tell you from their own experience what the bottom of the sea is like.

I have talked with a number of these pioneers of the deep frontier. This book tells their story: what they are seeing, hearing, feeling, and what scientific discoveries they are making on the bottom of the sea.

On his own repeated journeys to the bottom of the sea, Jim Cooney has learned to expect the unexpected. Not long ago, Cooney was aboard a submarine that was fast approaching the bottom off the coast of Georgia. She was half a mile down, far deeper than submarines before the 1960's had been able to dive. Cooney and the men with him were entering an unknown realm. They were prowling the depths, where only a few men had preceded them. They were exploring the bottom of the sea, doing their part in opening up a vast territory that covers seven-tenths (70.8 percent) of the globe.

The submarine carrying Cooney was the *Aluminaut*, the biggest (51 feet long, 70 tons) of the world's new deep-diving submarines and the one that can dive the deepest (15,000 feet). Cooney, today a pilot of General Dynamics' Star submarines, was engineering technician on this trip.

As *Aluminaut* dropped rapidly toward the sea floor, Cooney and his shipmates crowded at her viewports to see what was there. They switched on the high-intensity tungsten iodide lights that, from a boom extending forward from *Aluminaut's* bow, light up the depths. The bottom they quickly landed on was different from any other sea floor they had seen. It was unexpected.

"It was just like dropping into a large asphalt parking lot," Cooney said. "It was a flat black pavement."

Art Markel, the general manager of *Aluminaut*, was along on the dive. "It resembled a blacktop road," he told me. "The Gulf Stream currents evidently keep the pavement here swept clear of sediment."

Aluminaut was on the Blake Plateau, on the bottom of the Atlantic Ocean off the Southeast Coast of the United States.

She next did something that no naval submarines and few deep-diving submarines can do. She rolled over the paved bottom of the sea, just as a car rolls along a paved road.

"We have three wheels we can attach," Markel explained. "The wheels are bolted on by divers before we go down. They provide a means of maintaining a set distance off the bottom with a minimum of power." Two of the wheels are beneath *Aluminaut's* bow; one is at her stern. *Aluminaut* touched her rubber-tired wheels to the sea floor, and away she went.

Aluminaut then had to bring back the evidence of what her men had seen with their own eyes: a sample of the black pavement. Two 9-foot-long, hydraulically operated mechanical arms broke off a chunk of the pavement and stowed it in a big metal basket beneath the bow. Reynolds International, Inc., the owners of *Aluminaut*, say the arms work much like your own. Each can lift 4,000 pounds, and yet the 8-inch-long fingers can delicately pick up an object the size of a golf ball or the thinness of a pencil from the bottom of the sea.

"Each mechanical arm," says Cooney, "is an engineer's and technician's delight. It is simple. It is fantastic what it will do."

Aluminaut brought back into port a 168-pound sample of the pavement, believed to be the biggest specimen of its type ever intentionally raised from the ocean bottom and retained. What could have been the record was a 300-pounder brought up accidentally in a tangle of cables by a cable ship. The men on that ship, not being oceanographers or geologists, did not recognize the significance of their specimen and so dumped right back into the ocean the biggest rock ever hauled up from the depths.

The sample brought home by *Aluminaut* was analyzed. It turned out to be 40 percent manganese and 24 percent phosphate.

"The U.S.," Cooney said, "now imports 90 percent of its manganese, used in hardening steel. Here there's better than 1,000 square miles of manganese, just lying on the bottom untouched."

Added Markel: "Besides manganese, we found on the Blake Plateau gray sands deposited long ago. We were seeking heavy metal sands that might contain gold, silver, or titanium." Titanium is a metal used in spaceships and supersonic planes. Some engine parts of the huge new 490-passenger Boeing 747 also are titanium. Another use for titanium is in deep-diving submarines, for ribbing and for stiffening steel.

Around the edges of the pavement that *Aluminaut* rolled over, her men found more phosphate (phosphate is a valuable fertilizer) and potato-sized pieces of manganese. These manganese nodules are also found over much of the deep (two or three miles) bottom of the sea; they are too deep to be brought up in any quantity. On the Blake Plateau, only half a mile down, they may be easier to mine.

"In the past," said Cooney, "surface ships would send down buckets and bring up samples of what was on the bottom. Instead, we dived down to see."

Earlier reports from surface ships had indicated that there were minerals on the Blake Plateau. What the *Aluminaut* crew saw made it appear that there was a very large deposit indeed. On the bottom of the sea, they could see the wide extent of the mineral deposit. The Blake is a big plateau. It extends from Cape Hatteras, off North Carolina, to just north of Miami, Florida. It is too early to say yet, but *Aluminaut* may have helped make one of the world's great mineral strikes.

The Blake Plateau recently was investigated and mapped by the United States Geological Survey of the Department of the Interior and the Woods Hole Oceanographic Institution. On November 21, 1967, the Geological Survey announced: "Two billion tons of phosphatic nodules and over one billion tons of manganese-iron and phosphate-bearing materials lie on the sea bottom off the Georgia coast." To the Geological Society of America, Dr. Frank T. Manheim of the Geological Survey said: "Although these submarine deposits are much thinner and lower in grade than deposits now being exploited on the land, their great extent, closeness to land, and shallow depth may ultimately permit their economic use." In 1968, Dr. Vincent E. McKelvey of the Geological Survey pointed to the bottom of the sea as a future source of raw materials: "Even if only a fraction of the ocean basins contain usable deposits, the great extent of the basins insures a tremendous supply of useful minerals, including oil, phosphate, gold, diamonds, and manganese oxides."

The U.S. Coast and Geodetic Survey announced it was beginning a number of cruises over the Blake Plateau by its new ocean-exploring surface ship, *Discoverer*, to learn the extent of the minerals there. Bruce Grant, an oceanographer from the Land and Sea Interaction Laboratory at Norfolk, Virginia, said *Discoverer* would use deep-sea cameras to photograph the deposits and rock dredges to haul manganese nodules aboard ship. Besides manganese, the nodules contain nickel, iron, cobalt, and copper, Grant said. The nodules vary in size from micronodules to small-boulder-size, sometimes bigger. At Columbia University's Lamont Geological Observatory, I looked at some. They were knobby rocks; in color they were either black, silver, orange, black-and-white, or black-and-orange. Dr. John L. Mero, an authority on the nodules, has said that 20 to 50 percent of the South Pacific's ocean floor is covered with them, and in some areas, they are as thick as a cobblestone pavement. If they can be mined on the Blake Plateau, they may eventually be mined in deeper seas.

Sometimes the unexpected that Jim Cooney encounters in the depths of the sea is something unknown—a mystery.

17

On several of *Aluminaut's* dives there was the large object in the depths that kept darting around, ahead of, and behind the submarine, drawing close, then moving away.

It showed up on the sonar. "Tracking it," said Cooney, who was frustrated at the time, "was like tracking an unidentified flying object, or flying saucer. One moment the object would be in front of us, then it would dart off.

"Sometimes the image would follow us for four hundred or five hundred feet, then would dodge away, then would open the gap between us. We tried chasing it several times. We never caught up with it. We didn't know what it was that appeared to be attacking us. We had no idea what it was."

The solution came eventually from the company, Straza, that provided *Aluminaut's* sonar. Cooney told the story: "Our sonar emits a pulse continually and we get a return pitch. All this sound is recorded on tape. The Straza company analyzed the return pitch. It was the sound returned by something loosely held together. It is virtually certain that we know today what it was: It was schools of fish."

Dr. Clarence P. Idyll, of the University of Miami's Institute of Marine Science, and an expert on shrimp, took an *Aluminaut* trip 1,800 to 2,500 feet down in the Florida Straits and saw the unexpected: royal red shrimp and shrimp that are 9 to 10 inches long. (A shrimp 2 feet long lives in brackish and salt water near Miami, according to Craig Phillips, director of the National Aquarium. He has netted it by night. Its ruby eyes in his flashlight beam, he says, "were the most impressive invertebrate eyes I have ever seen.") "On the bottom," Dr. Idyll said, "we also saw skates, fairly large fish, several species of eels, and a surprising number of large squids." He also saw hatchetfish (a deep-dwelling luminescent fish), crabs, and a dense population of plankton (the tiny animals and plants that drift by the billions and billions throughout the sea). *Aluminaut* at the time was 25 miles from Miami and was cruising 5 to 10 feet above the bottom of the sea.

Jim Cooney, like virtually all the pilots who drive (that's the proper word for it) deep-diving submarines, came right out of the Navy and its submarines. "My background," he says, "is five years in nuclear submarines and three years in submarine school. The Navy spent $75,000 to educate me. I was on *Skate* two years, and about two on *Skipjack*, at the time the world's fastest atomic submarine."

No United States military submarine ever had viewports for you to look out of and see for yourself what was in the depths or on the bottom of the sea. As he watched one day through an *Aluminaut* viewport, Cooney saw what was probably the most unexpected sight he has ever seen in Davy Jones's locker. This was the oceanic equivalent of the elephant graveyard.

The elephant graveyard—a place where elephants supposedly go to die—has long been rumored to exist on land. It is a myth, a legend, a story that explorers of Africa and Asia have long sought to explain. They have looked for the elephant graveyard in countless jungles. They never have found it.

Aluminaut discovered something like it, on the bottom of the sea, beneath 2,000 feet of water and underneath the Gulf Stream, between Miami and Fort Lauderdale, Florida.

What *Aluminaut* came upon was a graveyard of those large sea mammals that are considered related to the elephants, the dugongs. Dugongs, up to 1,000 pounds in weight, are sea creatures whose face and woman-like breasts may, over the centuries, have caused sailors to believe in mermaids. They are said to suckle their young, on the surface, while sitting upright and holding them against a breast with a flipper.

"We were operating demonstration dives six miles offshore," Cooney said to me, "maybe two thousand feet down. We went down in the area several times. This time we went down and found fossil dugong bones—literally scattered all over the bottom, as though someone had thrown a wastebasket in an office.

"We at first thought they were odd-shaped rocks. We retrieved two with our mechanical arms. Dr. Kelly Brooks of the University of Florida told us what they were. They were dated at twenty-five million years old. The dugong lives in shallow water, so the bones indicate the coastline of Florida extended farther out twenty-five million years ago."

Cooney chuckled. "That's a sea-story type of story, isn't it?" he asked. He meant a sailor's tale no one would believe. "You never know," he said. "In my business, you never know what you'll see, from one day to the next."

The Deepest Submarine

2

He had just piloted a submarine to the deepest bottom of the sea a submarine ever had reached. His voice was calm. That did not mean there was no enthusiasm in his voice. There was. His exultation was undiminished by the 3,000 miles of phone wire between San Diego, California, and New York City.

Larry Shumaker had taken his boat, the spanking new 39-foot-10-inch-long, shark-shaped *Deep Quest*, down to 8,310 feet deep, 2,010 feet deeper than any submarine ever had dived before. The record that Shumaker had broken was his own: Six weeks earlier, he had piloted *Deep Quest* to the previous world record depth for submarines, 6,300 feet. Before that, *Aluminaut* had held the record, 6,250 feet.

At 8,310 feet down, Shumaker had reached the bottom of the sea in the abyss of the Pacific Ocean. The date was February 28, 1968. *Deep Quest* was 93 miles southwest of San Diego, California. Along with Shumaker, who is chief pilot of the submarine, were two other pilots, Glenn Minard and Don Saner, and Rear Admiral P. E. "Pete" Summers, United States Navy (Ret.), who helped design *Deep Quest* and is her program manager.

Shumaker looked out *Deep Quest's* viewports at a place no man ever had visited—a scene no man ever had seen.

"We saw fish and bottom-dwelling animals. Plantlike animals, with blossoms on their stems; these are hydrozoans that stick up from the bottom. They sit on what look like stalks of some sort of flowering plant. But they're animals. The actual form of these hydrozoans was a little bit different from any we'd seen on our earlier, shallower dives.

"I spotted holothurians, or sea cucumbers. A couple of the holothurians I saw seemed different, too, from shallower ones. I thought they seemed a little flatter.

"There were only a few brittle stars.

"There is always on these dives," he said, "something new. Always something you haven't seen before. So far, however, I haven't been startled. So far I haven't seen anything I can't relate to something I have seen before. I have not yet seen the *Deepstar* monster. But I keep hoping."

The *Deepstar* monster is a huge, unidentified fish seen on the bottom of the Pacific by Joe Thompson, pilot of *Deepstar 4000*.

Pete Summers stared out at the same bottom-of-the-ocean seascape.

Summers is familiar with the Pacific Ocean. During World War II he roamed it as the commander of a submarine flotilla. He won so many medals that they say around the Lockheed Missiles and Space Company, which designed and built *Deep Quest*, that Summers has to be followed around by a man carrying a chest containing his medals. He has 14 campaign ribbons from World War II. His highest award was the Navy Cross with bronze star.

Summers had made a number of earlier dives to the bottom in submarines you can look out of, and he is at home in the depths. On this trip, he saw things he never had encountered before.

"I saw a creature, as an example," he told me, "that had a broad top and a flat belly. It was the same color as the sediment about it—quite unusual. It may have been lying in the sediment." The sediment was fine brownish-gray silt. He said there was on the bottom a fish about a foot long that looked something like a cod.

"I saw a varicolored fish through the viewport," he went on. He observed the same plantlike animals Larry Shumaker had seen—countless numbers of them. "The whole area was a plain, like a plain in the Midwest. The plants—only they were animals—grew out of the plain. They were about one-and-a-half feet tall. The creatures were beautiful and lily-like. We powered *Deep Quest* over and examined them. She's a tremendously mobile submarine—we could move in and look. They had stems at the side of their stalks. The top was a big, open thing; five or six petals to it. Their color was a kind of dull gray.

"I had never seen these plantlike animals before. I told an oceanographer about them right after we got back, and he said they might be an animal thought to be extinct. But we don't know."

Deep Quest's record-breaking deepest dive began when she left her surface support vessel, *Transquest,* at 7 A.M.

Transquest, a specially built, 108-foot-long support ship, has a split stern that is open to, and admits the sea. Inside the stern, an elevator lowered *Deep Quest* into the water. *Deep Quest* slipped silently out and beneath the surface.

She was tracked by sonar from a surface tracking boat. The sonar contact was lost when *Deep Quest* reached 6,000 feet down. But she was in contact all the time with *Transquest* by underwater telephone. The phone connection never was broken. "I was on the support ship," Bob Campbell told me. "The communications worked better than expected. Our voice communication was clear as a bell—just like you and me, talking on the phone."

Deep Quest began a long spiral to the bottom.

She can descend in circles or she can go down in a long straight slant. The morning was gray; her crew knew they were over a depth of 8,000-feet-plus; they wanted to stay exactly over water that deep and did not want to take a chance on getting into shallower water outside the immediate area.

The occasion was the first time *Deep Quest* had tried to reach her maximum operating depth of 8,000 feet.

Inside her, as the dive began, Larry Shumaker relaxed. "There's a lot of pressure on you before a dive like this begins," he said to me. "But once the dive starts, all the pressure's over."

The water grew black, but the blackness was relieved by the luminescence of sea animals—lights that glowed from countless sea creatures.

On this trip, luminescence was rarer than on the earlier 6,300-foot dive. "It seemed to taper off," Shumaker said. "The layers between one thousand and three thousand feet had the biggest concentration."

"Some of the luminescent stuff was small, some large," Pete Summers said. "As we dive, we're moving—it passes by pretty fast."

Periodically, *Deep Quest* turned on her lights. Her crew always tries to conserve her battery power, so she dives with her floodlights off a good deal of the time. "When we turned on the lights," Summers said, "we saw a tremendous amount of plankton—from tiny dots to sizes the end of your finger. This was especially true about midway down. The plankton cluttered the water. We also saw streamer jellyfish on the way down."

As *Deep Quest* neared the bottom, her lights were switched on. She parked on the sea floor. She rested on two skegs, 20 feet long and 5 feet apart, that let her sit on the sea floor without her outer hull touching the bottom at all.

"We called up the surface," Pete Summers said, "and gave our depth." Only bathyscaphes, which lack the maneuverability of submarines, had been deeper.

She planted a flag. Inside a compartment up forward, *Deep Quest* had an American flag held by a clasp. A door like an eyelid opened. An explosive bolt was exploded and released the clasp holding the flag. A weight at the lower end of the flag's stainless steel stem drew it down, upright, and waving, to rest on the sea floor.

Inside, the crew drank to each other with Cokes.

As the sub rested on the bottom, the men took stock of their position. There was very little current detected where *Deep Quest* sat down. The men then cruised along, circled, and moved toward the lily-like creatures and took close looks at them. Four or five times the sub parked on the bottom.

The climb back brought *Deep Quest* to the surface at 3:30 P.M., after eight and one-half hours underwater. She was six or seven thousand yards from *Transquest*—quite a distance from the support ship. "We were a little concerned about getting so far away," Shumaker said, "but we were free to come up as fast as we could. We didn't have to worry about a ship over our heads."

Deep Quest nosed into *Transquest's* open stern and onto the elevator. The elevator raised her up and out of the water.

"We certainly were excited," said Bob Campbell, "after the dive was completed. Everybody came up and shook hands with the crew. Everybody was thankful the men had got back safely."

I had talked with Larry Shumaker before about the earlier 6,300-foot dive, made by *Deep Quest* on January 12, 1968, also in the Pacific, off San Diego. That one, he said, "was the first time we'd been able to put the boat into the automatic mode. After once we submerged, we picked out a course and angle at which I wanted to descend, put the pilot in automatic mode—steering, speed, and angle. In effect, I put my hands in my pocket."

But he watched his instruments. He watched the view through the ports, as he always does on *Deep Quest's* dives. Along with him on this trip were Don Saner, Robert K. R. Worthington, and Harold Criger, all of the Lockheed Ocean Systems Organization.

The men went through alternating layers of dark and then luminescent ocean. "The luminescence tends to be stratified," Shumaker said. "It's like a sky full of stars. The undersea lights are always in motion, always moving around, in every direction. Some animals are moving under their own power, some are drifting with the current.

"As you pass close by an animal, there seems to be something about the movement or approach of the submarine that affects him. He'll brighten, or almost flash.

"The luminescent creatures are mostly bluish and white. Somewhere maybe between blue and green. Everything seems pretty much the same—that blue-green or blue-white light."

He can't be sure, Shumaker says, when he switches on the floodlights, that the animals he then sees are those that provide the luminescence. "You never are sure that what you see with the lights is what you saw without them."

He thinks he knows, though, what luminescent light is made by euphausiids—small shrimplike animals that make up much of the krill eaten as their regular diet by the world's biggest whales.

"The euphausiids," he believes, "create a spiky flash. It looks like a point with five or six thin lines coming out—like a spark you might strike on metal—only that bluish-white color."

Deep Quest, Shumaker tells me, is almost always steady. No turbulence. No rocking or rolling or yawing. Shumaker thinks most deep-diving submarines are steady because there is not much turbulence or rough water in the depths. "A rocking motion," he says, "shows some fault in the boat or the control system. The ocean's depths are pretty slow. You don't have the currents or updrafts you do in an airplane. In the top one hundred fifty feet or so of the ocean you feel wave motion from the surface. But only in the top one hundred fifty feet.

"Once we made a fast simulated emergency ascent. We started off slowly. By the time we had gotten to eight hundred to one thousand feet below the surface, the boat was moving rapidly. When we hit the surface, coming up at about a twenty-five-degree angle, *Deep Quest* actually planed along the surface some fifty feet, like a speedboat. She threw up spray at the bow.

"But we came up just as steady as a rock."

At 6,300 feet down, *Deep Quest's* crew found a greenish-gray bottom of plain silt. No rocks. On this trip, her underwater phone conked out. This is almost to be expected, because of thermal conditions in the sea. But Pete Summers, this time on the bridge of *Transquest* on the surface, had a worrying time. The phone never did come back till the sub was on the surface.

"On the bottom," said Shumaker, "we saw rattail fish. The rattails twelve to fourteen inches long were the biggest animals we saw. We saw a conglomeration of starfish. We saw sea pens. Sea pens stick up out of the bottom like dried-up goldenrod; their stalks come up out of the bottom. Nevertheless, sea pens are animals, not plants. Some sea pens had starfish clustered on them like tree leaves. They looked a little like decorated Christmas trees. I've been told of some cases where sea pens and starfish are symbiotic; you never find one without the other. But I've also seen sea pens without starfish.

"There was evidence of burrowing animals. Worms and all kinds of little animals live in the bottom. We saw little heaps of sediment piled up where animals had dug in."

He saw, 6,300 feet down, a five-gallon bucket rusted out. It had not attracted a colony of animals and fish. This surprised him. "I thought fish would swarm around it," he said. "In a previous dive, we ran across a piece of pipe nine inches in diameter and found it had become a fish haven; the fish increased around it."

When *Deep Quest* came up—with no communications—the Coast Guard was asked to keep an eye out for her. She surfaced within view of *Transquest*.

After the 8,310-foot dive, *Transquest* brought *Deep Quest* back into San Diego. There on the pier the crew saw the best sight of all: their wives. The wives brought champagne for everybody. The girls also provided a four-piece band to welcome back *Deep Quest* with Navy music. Another thing awaited Larry Shumaker in San Diego: congratulatory telegrams from competitive deep-diving submarines.

Larry Shumaker told me how he felt at this point: "Just fine. Everything went well. We exceeded our design depth by 300 feet. We're all real pleased. I'm doubly pleased. We have proven out the thing I've been waiting for a long, long time."

At 8,310 feet down, *Deep Quest* had been under a water pressure of approximately 3,500 pounds per square inch or more than 230 times the 15 PSI at sea level.

"I have the strain-gauge readings before me now," Larry Shumaker said as he talked with me. "There were no weak spots in the hull. We've got a going boat now.

"This is the submarine we've been waiting for. We can stay down twenty-four hours and be comfortable—and we have done so on a shallower dive. We can maneuver at from one-half to four and a half knots. We can take a good-sized payload—seven thousand pounds of scientific instruments, for instance. We have power to spare. We have a fully-integrated system, complete with the single-stick control of the ship. Now we have reached our maximum design depth.

"The people who worked on this dive are certainly thrilled. It's a major milestone in our progress." Larry Shumaker did not say it, but to reach 8,310 feet down also was a milestone in (1) the history of submarines, and (2) mankind's thousands of years of effort to live and work in the ocean. The depths of the ocean, to over 8,000 feet down, almost entirely unvisited and unseen by man, would be *Deep Quest's* to explore.

"It's a New World"

3

"I could look out and see the bottom," Gene Rodgers said. "That's the big thing about deep-diving submarines.

"I had made many dives in Navy submarines and could not look out. Now, in deep-diving submarines with viewports, it's like flying around the moon in a space capsule. It's a new world."

Rodgers, 39, of Ledyard, Connecticut, took a Star submarine, *Star III*, down off Cape May, New Jersey, to look through her viewports at a cable. He and *Star III* were doing a job of inspection for a telephone company.

Gene Rodgers' new world on the bottom of the sea unrolled almost explosively before his gaping eyes.

"We went down around eighteen hundred feet off Cape May," he said to me, "and at that depth we saw life similar to plants. At eighteen hundred feet deep, we had all kinds of plantlike growth, all different colors, reddish, blue and white and so on, up to two feet high. It was beautiful.

"The fish at eighteen hundred feet deep are a red color, almost orange. They would hang around the rocks. We saw many about a foot and a half long. The colors showed up in our lights. When we were without external lights, things showed up dark and light—no colors."

Rodgers' naval service was at first on aircraft carriers and shore stations (Saipan was one). Then in 1949 he got onto a submarine support ship. Here he heard so much and learned so much about submarines that, he tells you, "in fifty-five I joined them. I was on the old fleet subs, *Spikefish, Conger, Entemedor.*"

Rodgers and other *Star III* pilots had no trouble locating the cable. They found it, got close to it (several feet above it), and followed it to sea, all the way to 300 fathoms (1,800 feet), or past the edge of the continental shelf and well down onto the continental slope as it slants toward the ocean abyss. They found the cable in good shape. They also found it was inhabited.

Inhabited by lobsters. They saw so many lobsters and such big ones that the *Star III* men told me about them. They couldn't stop talking about them. "They looked," Gene Rodgers said, "as though they weighed about twenty pounds. They were two to two and a half feet long. They semed to stay around the cable. The lobsters seemed to tunnel under it."

Star III, launched in 1966, was built by the Electric Boat Division of General Dynamics for the company's own exploration of the ocean and for leasing out for jobs beneath the sea. She takes to her maximum depth of 2,000 feet a pilot and an observer. A 7.5-horsepower electric motor in her stern propels the 24½-foot-long *Star III* at from 1 knot normal speed to 5 knots full speed, when she is submerged.

Star III has company—and competition—as she and her men roam the depths and make voyages to the bottom of the sea. This is the United States' lineup of deep-diving submarines, as of 1968:

• *Star I* and *Star II* of General Dynamics' Submarine Test and Research fleet. *Star I* carries one man to a depth of 200 feet. *Star II* can dive 1,200 feet. She can explore all of the continental shelves—the shallow areas next to the continents—in the world, which amount to an area roughly as large as Africa.

- Reynolds International's *Aluminaut.*
- Lockheed's *Deep Quest.*
- The Litton Industries'-Woods Hole Oceanographic Institution's-United States Navy's *Alvin,* which can dive 6,000 feet and has done so a number of times.
- *Deepstar 4000,* built in France under the supervision of Jacques-Yves Cousteau for the Westinghouse Electric Corporation, and already operated off United States' Pacific, Gulf, and Atlantic coasts. She can dive 4,000 feet, and often has.
- The Scripps Institution's (formerly the Navy's) *Deep Jeep* which, like *Star III,* dives to 2,000 feet. *Deep Jeep* and *Alvin* are research submarines the Navy has owned outright. Most others are privately owned and have been produced by individual men or business firms without government help. But the Navy has leased the majority of them and is by far the world's most experienced operator of the new ships that prowl Davy Jones's locker.
- Ed Link and John H. Perry's *Deep Diver. Deep Diver* can dive 1,350 feet and can let men step out on the bottom, and has done so, though at depths considerably short of 1,350 feet.
- A fleet of John H. Perry's Cubmarines. Perry, a pioneer manufacturer of small undersea boats, has seen his craft become well-known since 1962. For one thing, they have been on the "Flipper" television series. When I asked Perry how he happened to build the subs, he said he had been a scuba diver, liked to see what was beneath the sea—but wanted to keep dry. Most of his boats are for one or two men and dive 1,000 feet or less. *Shelf Diver* (to 600 feet) is his latest.
- The *Deep Ocean Work Boat, DOWB,* by AC Electronics, a division of General Motors. *DOWB* can carry two men, support them underwater for 65 hours, dive to 6,500 feet. She can hover and maneuver and has a highly sophisticated mechanical arm.
- The American Submarine Company's 13-foot-long *Amersub 300* (to 300 feet) and the 13-foot-long *Amersub 600* (to 600 feet). The company, in Lorain, Ohio, says anyone can "navigate the deep" in its boats. "No special clothing or equip-

ment is required of the passenger or operator, and no supporting crew or equipment is needed."

• *Asherah*, formerly one of the Star boats. She carries two men, dives 650 feet, and generally stays down around ten hours. She is 16 feet long and tadpole-shaped. She is named for the ocean goddess of history's first recorded seafarers, the Phoenicians.

Launched in 1964, *Asherah* first found and explored sunken wrecks and archaeological sites in the Aegean Sea for the University of Pennsylvania Museum. Then she made a series of dives for the Bureau of Commercial Fisheries Biological Laboratory, Honolulu, Hawaii. "The scientists from the laboratory in Honolulu who made the dives aboard the *Asherah*," says the bureau, "write of their observations with a cool dispassion; they speak of them with excitement, for what they saw has been seen by very, very few men. They found the sloping sandy plain (the bottom of the sea off Oahu) featureless and almost barren of life, except where it was dotted by coral growth or rocky rubble: there hosts of creatures congregated. The rocky ledges 10 to 60 feet high that interrupted the plain were surrounded by clouds of colorful fishes. Above these bottom-dwelling species swam schools of fishes of the mid-depths." There was an abrupt cliff that swept "nearly vertically downward, far deeper than the range of the little research craft.

"Wherever the steep face of the limestone underwater cliff afforded a foothold, things were growing, and small, feeding fishes were swarming around them like bees about a blossoming tree. It was at this considerable depth, about 500 feet, that a scientist aboard the *Asherah* made what was perhaps the single most important observation of the dives. There he saw skipjack tuna feeding on fishes an inch or so long. The depth to which the skipjack tuna traveled had never been known before. The fish are known almost entirely from their brief visits to the surface in pursuit of prey." The skipjack is a valuable fish for food, and the scientists of the Bureau of Commercial Fisheries have been studying its behavior underwater in the Pacific —if men know its behavior, they will be more likely to catch it.

"In crevices and ledges along the cliff face," says the bureau, "were seen spiny lobsters of a size rarely caught in Hawaii. Like the skipjack tuna, other fishes, such as snapper, amberjack, and wahoo, patrolled the cliff. In all, more than 100 species of fish were seen on the *Asherah* dives. There were literally millions of the small forage fish upon which the larger, commercially important species feed."

In the fall of 1965, Donald W. Strasburg, from the Bureau of Commercial Fisheries, aboard *Asherah*, became the first man to see in its location on the bottom of the sea the rare and valuable red coral. Of 2,500 known species of coral, the bureau says, only one or two are considered of gem quality. In 1840, a sample of the red coral of gem quality was obtained by the American geologist James D. Dana, who was with the United States Exploring Expedition. His specimen came from the Hawaiian Islands. Strasburg saw the coral on the leeward side of the island of Oahu. Later, University of Hawaii scientists found beds of the precious coral between Oahu and Molokai. Still later, 500 feet down, the coral was brought up by tangle gear. And by 1966, Christmas shoppers in Honolulu, as the result, were offered a novelty available nowhere else in the United States: jewelry made from a pale, luminous pink coral called "angelskin coral," the red coral.

The red coral is one of the most valuable bottom-of-the-sea discoveries so far of precious gems for jewelry. Another: diamonds mined in the ocean off South West Africa; most of them are turning out to be gem stones. Rivers wash them into the sea, D. Vincent Manson, a South African minerals man, told me at the American Museum of Natural History. Weather, waves, and seawater work on them, and those diamonds that survive the rough treatment are especially fine.

All of these deep-diving submarines (including *Deepstar 4000*) are American. There are also in existence or being built British, French, Russian, Swiss, Japanese, and Canadian deep-diving submarines. One small craft pointed the way: Jacques-Yves Cousteau's diving saucer (also called *Soucoupe* or *SP-300*) that would go 1,000 feet down. The diving saucer appeared in 1959. Cousteau in 1968 added two jet-driven one-man submarines, two tons each, to dive 2,000 feet. They will work together as a team. He calls them "tiny hot rods" or "sea fleas."

The U.S. Coast and Geodetic Survey has announced that its next new ocean survey ship, *Researcher*, will be the first Coast Survey ship to be able to handle deep-sea research submarines. She will have a 20-ton crane to lower them into and lift them out of the sea.

What amounts to another fleet of deep-diving submarines is on the drawing boards or is being built. Westinghouse has *Deepstar 2000* for a 2,000-foot depth. Two new, improved versions of *Alvin*, *Autec I* and *Autec II*, are being completed at the Electric Boat Division of General Dynamics. Reynolds International is thinking about more *Aluminauts*. The Sunship Company, of Chester, Pennsylvania, is building the *Guppy* for 2,000 feet.

North American Rockwell's Ocean Systems Operations is assembling the *Beaver Mark IV*, for depths to 2,000 feet. I saw a full-sized model at a Marine Technology Society convention. *Beaver* will have a crew of two, and one day may let divers off to roam the 1,000-foot-deep sea bottom. She will be 25 feet long, 8½ feet high, 9½ feet in beam, and weigh 27,000 pounds dry. She will have two especially versatile manipulator arms. In some earlier research submarines, tools are placed in the hands of the arms before a submarine submerges. *Beaver* will carry her tools in a chest mounted on her hull; her arms will be capable of reaching into the chest for the tools they need. She will be able to cut cables, wield wrenches, and use stud guns, jet pumps, grinding wheels, and wire brushes. A 120-volt main battery and a 30-volt auxiliary battery will power her motors to drive three propellers, with which she will move, maneuver, and hover. Her controls are portable: The pilot can move them to any of ten viewports and steer and control her while he looks out. *Beaver's* manipulator arms also are portable and can be moved to any viewport.

The Navy Yard, Portsmouth, New Hampshire, is building

a diesel-and-electric ocean-exploring submarine, the *Dolphin*, number 555. She will be a big one: 152 feet long, 18 feet in beam, and will displace 930 tons. At General Dynamics, the *NR-1*, the Navy's first nuclear-powered deep-diving boat is on the slipway. With the ability to remain submerged indefinitely, due to nuclear power, the *NR-1* could revolutionize exploring the bottom of the sea.

By far the deepest-diving of the United States' future bottom-dwelling submarines will be the 20,000-footers. *Deepstar 20,000*, planned by Westinghouse, apparently will be the first privately owned submarine to be able to go nearly four miles down. The Navy plans a fleet of its own 20,000-foot submarines to rescue men in disabled submarines, to search for lost objects, and to recover them—and also to do some exploration of the ocean's depths.

The depths of the ocean have been called inner space. Deep-diving vessels have been called, by the Gulf Universities Research Corporation (a group of universities on the Gulf of Mexico that are interested in oceanography), "inner-space capsules." Inside the inner-space capsules a new breed of men is developing. Jacques-Yves Cousteau calls the new breed the "oceanauts." The United States Navy, which has just begun training officers and crews for deep-diving vessels, calls them "hydronauts" (a name reserved for pilots of deep submersibles). Hydronauts or oceanauts, they are the first men in the history of mankind who are becoming familiar with the bottom of the sea. As Gene Rodgers said, they can "look out and see the bottom."

The Fish
That Rode
a Submarine

4

"On *Star III*," Al Rutherford said, "we were working off New England for the U.S. Navy Underwater Sound Laboratory when the underwater lights outside the boat, which were turned on, started blinking on and off.

"We were about eleven hundred feet down off the continental shelf. I thought something was wrong with the lights, but I could find nothing wrong.

"Then I saw what was the trouble. I looked through the forward viewport—a small, round window we have in the bow of *Star III*. We were being attacked by squids—by hundreds of squids.

"They were small ones, four to six inches long. As they attacked us, they squirted their ink, like the sepia of cuttlefish or India ink, into the water. Sometimes there was so much black ink squirted at us that the lights were blotted out."

Star III is the same submarine that had taken Gene Rodgers to inspect the telephone cable (and those lobsters) off New Jersey. The squid, *Star III's* attacker, is a ten-armed relative of the ten-armed cuttlefish and the eight-armed octopus. Squids come in many species and sizes all the way up to the giant squid that may be 60 feet or even longer. The common Atlantic Coast squid is a small one, about a foot long. "No one knows," Ralph Buchsbaum and Lorus J. Milne write in *The Lower Animals*, "how many squids live in the sea. The number must be enormous. . . . Man's nets are too slow-moving and too obvious to fast-swimming squids for any reasonable sample to be caught from large boats on the ocean's surface." The squids jet-propel themselves by pumping water through a tube. With their jets, they get power enough to shoot 40 feet into the air, the National Geographic Society says, gliding a distance of 100 feet. Sometimes they land on decks of ships. Their bursts of speed, says Sir Alister Hardy in *The Open Sea*, make them "probably the fastest of all aquatic animals."

Star III had no weapons to fight a bath of ink, and so Al Rutherford did nothing. In time, the squids discovered *Star III* was not harming them. "After the squids got on to us," Rutherford continued, "they hung motionless in the water. Perfectly still. We looked out and saw one after another, hanging quiet.

"Then we noticed a few red shrimp in the water. Sometimes a shrimp would get about four feet away from a squid. Then —Zzzzzztt! The squid would shoot—jet—through the water. Then we would see the squid where the shrimp had been a second before.

"No shrimp!"

Alfred Lien Rutherford, 39 years old, is the chief pilot of the Star boats—*Star I*, *Star II*, and *Star III*. He has made about 300 dives in them. Before that, he tested nuclear submarines. When *Aluminaut* was to be built, he says, "It looked like a tough job." He applied to work on it, and did. Then he went on to the Star boats.

Star III kept right on working in the same New England coast area where the squids had squirted their ink at her. She continued to have company.

"At about twelve hundred feet one day," Rutherford told me, "we ran into lantern fish." This time it was not by the hundreds, as it had been with the squids—it was by the thousands and thousands.

"They tried to get out of our way. They tried to run away. They got in a hurry. The lantern fish rubbed against each other or against the submarine.

"Their scales, some of them, fell off. The scales were luminescent. They looked like a million stars."

The big-eyed lantern fish is like a minnow in size: from 3 to 6 inches long when fully grown. It is one of the most common fish in the ocean. The brown, gray, silver, or iridescent blue lantern fish exist in great numbers in the upper levels of the deep sea. Their silvery flanks may be tinged with pink or green. They are, though their species vary in different regions, everywhere in the ocean, according to Dr. Richard H. Backus of the Woods Hole Oceanographic Institution on Cape Cod, Massachusetts. (The commonest fish in the sea is probably the bristlemouth, or cyclothone—a fish a few inches long whose mouth bristles with teeth.)

Instead of swimming away from *Star III*, many of the lantern fish became passengers aboard the submarine. They squeezed aboard.

"They seem to like dark places," Rutherford went on. "They crowded into our ballast tank. They got into the hatch over our heads and snuggled down in it."

So many lantern fish got into the hatch that, when *Star III* came to the surface, Al and the man with him could not open it to climb out. *Star III* had to be hoisted aboard by her tender so that the lantern fish could be scooped out of the hatch. They were 18 inches deep in it.

The next day, at the same 1,200-foot depth, the same thing happened all over again.

There were still more lantern fish the third day. They had discovered the drains and other tight places in *Star III* into which they could jam themselves.

"After those three days," Al said, "*Star III* stank like a fish market."

Star III made a magnetic survey 50 feet above the bottom in the same New England area. "We were running northwest,"

Al explained. "As we came up the shelf, we saw many large crabs—they look to me like Alaskan king crabs, or something halfway between spider crabs and king crabs. I'd say they were about eight inches across. I would say you couldn't move ten feet in any direction without running into a pair of them.

"The crabs were aware of us. They turned and put up their pincers at the submarine in a defensive maneuver. Most of them scurried to get away.

"There were numerous deep eels, two to three feet long, sighted also in this area, on the bottom eleven hundred to twelve hundred feet down.

"The floor there was very beautiful and fascinating. There were many pink-and-white sea anemones that grew up to eighteen or twenty inches. In the light they were beautiful. I could imagine flying over the Sahara Desert and seeing oases —these anemones were the oases."

Al Rutherford's oases are some of the most unusual creatures in the ocean. The sea anemone is an animal that looks like a plant, especially an aster or a chrysanthemum. It is an animal with a hollow, cylindrical, tree-trunk-like body. (The giants, on the Great Barrier Reef, off Australia, reach a diameter of 2 to 3 feet.) An opening on top is the mouth, surrounded by tentacles that are equipped with thousands of minute stinging threads wound up in tiny balls. When an animal or fish swims within reach of the tentacles, the balls unwind and lasso the animal or fish and poison and paralyze it. As if to demonstrate to men its power, a sea anemone 8 inches in diameter, at the Niagara Falls, New York, aquarium, not long ago unwound its tentacles and caught, killed, and devoured a 30-inch leopard shark.

Yet the anemone is the salvation of a tiny fish. "A certain 'Coral fish' of the East Indies, no bigger than a minnow, might fall a prey to endless foes," E. G. Boulenger wrote in *Life of the Ocean*, "but for possessing a sanctuary always within easy reach of its invertebrate host. The fish is coloured much like its huge patron, the anemone, in whose interior it habitually lives. Unscathed it sports amongst the sea flower's deadly tentacles, and on the least alarm darts down amongst them, deep into the monster's stomach easily, there to hide until the panic of the moment passes."

Anemones rest on the bottom of the sea. Some never move, but some can glide 3 to 4 inches an hour, on their bases, the thick, slimy disks at the bottoms of their bodies. One anemone glided one and a half feet in 24 hours. Some anemones live not on the sea floor, but on the shells of living crabs. They camouflage the crabs.

Sea anemones are hardy creatures. But they not only make a showplace of the bottom of the sea off New England. A new species has been hauled up, by trawl, from the utmost depths of the sea: from the sea bottom, almost seven miles down, of the Marianas Trench, off Guam. There they live in intense cold, pressure, and darkness.

One sea anemone may have been kept as a pet longer than any other pet, ever, anywhere. About 1827, an anemone was taken from a sea pool in the rocks at North Berwick, Scotland. On bits of oyster and mussel once or twice a week, and on daily changes of sea water, the anemone survived the deaths of four successive human owners. The anemone acquired a name —Granny, as you would expect—and died in 1887, 60 years after she had been brought from the sea (and no one knew how old she had been then). A newspaper, *The Scotsman*, gave Granny's death a notice that was half a column long—a length normally reserved for important citizens.

Al Rutherford saw other spectacular scenery from *Star III* when he dived in the Bahamas.

"My first experience off Nassau in *Star III*," Rutherford said, "we dove down a cliff with not quite a forty-five-degree slope. You go out a couple of thousand yards from the beach there and the bottom drops from thirty-two feet to three thousand feet.

"I was diving with Pete Khune, chief engineer for the New Providence Development Corporation, of the Bahamas. We were taking temperature readings at one-hundred-foot levels to two thousand feet down.

"We picked up a cliff at about fifteen hundred feet. You look to right and left. It seemed there were mountains all around you. Then you get into a gully and have to maneuver considerably to get out of it. You clear a boulder about house size. The light shows the boulder. Then you drop down another fifty to seventy-five feet and are in pitch-black water.

"Above the black water it was a kind of gray. There wasn't much color. What little color there was tended toward pinkish or yellow."

Gene Rodgers also piloted *Star III* in the Bahamas. Said he: "The most interesting thing I saw was that cliff. It went straight down and then it sloped out at a seventy-degree angle. It was mostly a jagged cliff just like a cliff on shore. It had little caves in it. The bottom at the foot of the cliff was kind of sandy. My passenger and I saw what we thought was a torpedo from one hundred feet above it. Yes, you could see one hundred feet down in that water. When we got down for a close look, it was a beer bottle."

"It's not only small submarines that are doing the job of exploring the sea," Rutherford says, "but larger ones as well. And what we'll be doing! We will be charting underwater mountain ranges. The things we're going to see will make the Grand Canyon look secondary. I feel privileged to be in this field—to be a part of it."

Rutherford told me about something seen recently off California.

"Siphonophores, jellyfish-like creatures," he said, "will attach themselves to each other in communities." In the Pacific, an oil company reported siphonophores joined in strings up to 70 feet long. That may be the world's biggest jellyfish-like beast. It may also be one of the sea serpents men keep sighting but never catch. You can't catch a giant siphonophore in a net. It falls apart and melts. A new tool, the slurp gun, has been invented; it may vacuum up some of the gelatin-like animals and collect some of the stuff they're made of so we can learn more about them.

The giant siphonophore proves that there are in the sea such things as animals that, while you watch, can disappear before your eyes.

The Discovery
of the
Sunken Galleon

5

The dives made by *Aluminaut* alone—she had made about 250 by 1968—are equal to anything the fertile mind of Jules Verne ever imagined for his *20,000 Leagues Under the Sea*.

In 1869, Verne, a Frenchman, startled the world with his best-selling novel about a purely imaginary submarine called the *Nautilus*. There were no submarines at the time. Not till 1900 would John Philip Holland, an American, build the first practical submarine. Meanwhile, Verne's fictional *Nautilus* cruised the depths, and her men gazed out through her windows into the deep water and at the bottom of the sea, and saw strange animals, weird landscapes, and sunken cities. The book seized the imagination of the public and has given generations of readers their idea of what the bottom of the sea is like. *20,000 Leagues* also kindled the imaginations of scientists and made them want to do in reality what Verne's characters did in fiction.

Now—in *Aluminaut* and other deep-diving craft—men can. They are doing it.

In *20,000 Leagues*, the men of the *Nautilus* find a sunken ship on the bottom of the sea. It looks like an "enormous black mass." They see the tattered sails and broken masts. They see other sunken vessels and their chains, anchors, and cannons.

In 1966, Art Markel, general manager of *Aluminaut*, gazed through a viewport and was startled: He was looking at a Spanish or Portuguese galleon from the 1400's—500 years ago. The ship still exists, although no one knew it before the *Aluminaut* crew saw her.

Markel saw the galleon as a clear outline about 350 feet down off southern Spain. *Aluminaut* was then helping the United States Navy in a search for a lost H-bomb. The bomb, in a tragic crash of Air Force planes, had fallen into the Mediterranean Sea. "We first detected the galleon with sonar," Markel said to me. "Then we saw her. She was well preserved, and was lying in a pile of rubble. She was about one hundred and fifty feet long, and was covered with light sediment. We saw things exposed—block and tackle, and cannon. The shapes of the cannon show the age of the ship."

Aluminaut during the hunt for the H-bomb could not tarry even over such a find as a galleon looking much as she did in the days of Columbus (who may have seen the same ship before she sank). "We spent no time there," Markel explained. "We surfaced in twenty minutes. We will have to study the ship to identify her."

The reason the ship is in such good shape, he says, is that the deeper the sea, the better it preserves many things. Below the light zone, below where sunlight penetrates, Art Markel says, you find that the sea is a preserver—"a safe-deposit box."

"We go below six hundred or seven hundred feet, and we find some things essentially as they went down. The only damage to them is worm holes. There are worms below the sunlight.

"For this reason, you can identify things in deep water that you can't in shallow water."

Markel, a 1948 graduate of the Naval Academy, was a football end and an All-America captain of the Navy's intercollegiate champion lacrosse team. He played three years against

Army in both sports. He went on to submarines and on to *Aluminaut*.

The galleon was one of the two most exciting things Markel ever has seen, he says, in his personal eyewitness exploration of the depths. The other: a spring—a gushing outflow of water—on the bottom of the sea. "We [*Aluminaut*] got heavy in the colder water coming out of the ground." The submarine was off Florida. "It appeared to be," he said, "like a spring you'd see on land."

"Far beneath the surface," said Professor Pierre Arronax, a scientist in *20,000 Leagues Under the Sea*, "I saw the swift and elegant porpoise, the indefatigable clown of the ocean."

Captain Bill Gray of the Miami, Florida, Seaquarium has captured alive probably more porpoises than any other man, and is an authority on them. He said they had been seen and photographed 400 feet down, the world's record for a deep dive for a porpoise. Art Markel in *Aluminaut* watched a porpoise break that world's record. So did two marine zoologists *Aluminaut* was carrying at the time.

"Off Miami," Markel said, "a porpoise followed us down. At six hundred feet we picked up something on our sonar directly ahead. We looked through a porthole. It was the porpoise, about thirty-nine or forty feet away." That incident was a contribution to science because it was, and is, the deepest-known porpoise dive.

Jules Verne's imaginary *Nautilus* was 232 feet long, 26 feet in breadth, and weighed 1,500 tons. *Aluminaut* is much smaller: 51 feet long, 70 tons in weight. The *Nautilus*, Verne wrote, sometimes cruised submerged at 12 knots. That's much faster than *Aluminaut's* 3.8 knots. The *Nautilus* was built of steel. *Aluminaut* is made of forged aluminum cylinders, each 40 inches long and 6½ inches thick, and has been called "a big roll of foil." Aboard the fictional *Nautilus*, electricity did all the cooking. It also does on *Aluminaut's* hot plate and coffee maker, which are all she has to cook with. Electricity propelled the

Nautilus beneath the sea as it does *Aluminaut*. *Aluminaut* is driven by two five-horsepower direct-current motors turning twin screws. She has an overhead propeller for hovering, ascending, or descending.

With her ability to dive 15,000 feet, or almost three miles, *Aluminaut* can go deeper than any submarine built before or since. She can reach over 60 percent of the ocean floor. The ocean, on the average, is around two and one-third miles deep.

Said the then Secretary of the Navy, Paul H. Nitze, at the launching of *Aluminaut* on September 2, 1964: "She will open to man undersea areas which have lain hidden in total darkness since the genesis of the planet."

Said J. L. Reynolds, her owner—she had been his dream: "Anyone who has read Jules Verne's *20,000 Leagues Under the Sea* can appreciate what this day means to me."

In *20,000 Leagues,* Professor Arronax often gazes out the windows of the *Nautilus* at the fish and other creatures in the sea. Through *Aluminaut's* four Plexiglas viewing ports in the bow—three look down, one looks forward—her crew watched fish in the Mediterranean off Spain. "We saw big fish there," Art Markel recalled. "They were much like groupers—very immobile, just lying under some rocks. They looked like five-hundred- or six-hundred-pounders." Half a mile down off Spain, Markel and the *Aluminaut* crew stared at red-and-white shrimp a foot long.

Jules Verne talked of "the transparency of the sea." Says Robert E. Serfass, captain in 1965 of *Aluminaut*: "We see anything fifty or sixty feet ahead of us."

Dr. W. K. Brooks of the University of Florida, who took a dive on *Aluminaut*, agreed. "Textbooks say you can't see at a depth of much more than six hundred feet," he said afterward. "I told them to keep the lights out till we reached a depth of one thousand feet, and we could see quite well for a distance of sixty to eighty feet."

Lights on Jules Verne's *Nautilus* lit up the sea, Verne wrote, "for half a mile in front." There were not then, and there are not now, any submarine lights that can light up the sea for any such distance. But when *Aluminaut's* powerful searchlights were turned on, said Art Markel, "we could see clearly for three hundred feet."

Aluminaut frequently carries scientists into the ocean depths. Dr. Harry Bennett of Louisiana State University said after his journey to the bottom of the sea that he was reminded of the first time he used another scientific tool, the microscope. With each tool, he said, he was amazed at what he saw.

Texas Tech's Dr. Dan E. Feray found *Aluminaut* comfortable—just like Jules Verne described the *Nautilus*. Said Dr. Feray: "We were unaware that we had left the surface, and we were unaware when we were sitting on the bottom. It was like working in a laboratory in your own office."

The Bureau of Commercial Fisheries' Harvey Bullis and William G. Anderson, aboard *Aluminaut*, found a seafood dinner 175 miles long. In water 120 to 150 feet deep, 30 miles offshore, between St. Augustine and Fort Pierce, Florida, they found mammoth beds of calico scallops.

Late in 1966, *Aluminaut* dived to do a job unimagined in Jules Verne's time a hundred years ago. Off St. Croix, Virgin Islands, she went down 3,150 feet to look for a 2,900-foot-long tangled skein of oceanographic instruments that had been lost the year before. The instruments were current meters—five of them. The buoy carrying them had broken loose, and the meters, all fastened to a cable, had sunk to the bottom. The whole costly system had been given up as lost, and its data written off.

A team from the Naval Oceanographic Office, which owned the meters, dived on *Aluminaut* to see what could be done. R. Frank Busby of the Oceanographic Office was the Navy project director.

Chief Pilot Robert H. Canary handled *Aluminaut*. The water over 3,000 feet down was pitch-black. It had to be floodlit by *Aluminaut's* lights. Then the bottom, the globigerina ooze (the remains of globigerinae, minute plankton animals) that covers vast amounts of the bottom of the sea, looked like mostly white sand.

It took *Aluminaut* one hour and 56 minutes on her first dive to find the 2,100-pound array of instruments.

Her second dive took 3 hours and 51 minutes because another cable was found on the bottom. To identify it, *Aluminaut's* two mechanical arms had to lift the cable in front of her viewing ports.

During this dive *Aluminaut* was caught in a current running down the bottom across descending steps of rock ledges. She circled back. She almost ran into a precipice that loomed out of the darkness. Skillful handling got her out of that; she surmounted the precipice.

To raise the instruments, Chief Pilot Canary went down with a coil of 2,000 feet of nylon line attached to *Aluminaut's* bottom.

One end of the line was fixed to her keel. On the other end there was a hook which engaged the current meters. Then *Aluminaut* moved to the surface, the coil unrolled, and a long line ran down to the instruments, hauling them up.

Aluminaut transferred her end of the nylon line to the tender *Privateer* on the surface. *Privateer* hoisted the delicate but heavy current meters on board.

It was the deepest search-and-recovery mission yet performed, and took *Aluminaut* a total of 12 hours and three minutes submerged time.

The current meters had been brought up from a deeper depth than that from which the H-bomb had been recovered off Spain, the previous deepest recovery of a lost object.

"The *Aluminaut's* maneuverability," Bob Canary said after the mission, "is beautifully precise. She sets down on the bottom like a feather, she turns beautifully, she trims out like a lady . . . and what more could you ask?" Canary, a former Navy chief with 23 years aboard Navy submarines, sits in a space-capsule-like seat amidships on the starboard side of the ship.

Frank Busby said the recovered current meters were in excellent condition and were in fact undamaged and operating when found. They yielded useful information.

"The *Aluminaut's* achievement," said Art Markel, "demonstrated that expensive instruments or other items of great value lost to ocean depths need not be considered Davy Jones's property."

Also off St. Croix, *Aluminaut* did a job that could not have been done before the days of deep-diving submarines: She made a survey of the bottom of the sea up to 3,600 feet down. What she surveyed—constantly mapping, making sub-bottom profiles, collecting bottom sediments, exploring, and taking stereo photographs—was the United States Navy's Atlantic Fleet Weapons Range. She inspected undersea installations for effects of corrosion. Frank Busby was again the project director, L. C. Morris was operations manager, and Chief Pilot Canary handled *Aluminaut*.

Jules Verne had the *Nautilus* make the deepest dive ever made in fiction in one of his most exciting scenes: "The *Nautilus* descended still lower, in spite of the great pressure. I felt the steel plates tremble at the fastenings of the bolts; its bars bent, its partitions groaned; the windows of the saloon seemed to curve under the pressure of the waters."

On the night of November 10-11, 1965, *Aluminaut* set the submarine depth record (only bathyscaphes had gone deeper) by diving 6,250 feet, one and one-quarter miles. The record she broke had been set shortly before by the *Alvin's* 6,000 feet. The record stayed until broken by *Deep Quest* in 1968.

"Veterans Day!" says *Aluminaut's* log. "All on board are U. S. Navy submarine veterans." The men aboard were Art Markel, Bob Serfass, Bob Canary, Dennison K. Breese, T. Robert Kendall, Jim Cooney, and Al Rutherford.

Aluminaut was that night 20 miles west of Great Abaco Island in the Bahamas. She went down part way at more than 100 feet a minute.

Cooney says he did not see much outside *Aluminaut* as

she descended on the deepest dive. "I was concerned with strain-gauge readings." He was watching what the enormous pressure of the water was doing to the hull. "I concentrated on the shape the hull was taking and the stress points in the hull and how the gauges reacted," he said. "It was quite interesting to watch."

It took *Aluminaut* four hours to go down.

At 1:10 in the morning, she reached her deepest point, 6,250 feet. "We are," says her log, "World's Deepest Diving Submarine." The men aboard had hot coffee from their coffee maker and meat sandwiches. They could not locate the bottom on a Fathometer—so there was plenty of water still beneath them. They could find no images whatever on sonar. They were, apparently, alone in the depths, floating in inner space, surrounded only by dark water.

Not quite alone, though. At their greatest depth, the men aboard got a phone call from J. Louis Reynolds, who was 1,000 miles away in Richmond, Virginia. Mr. Reynolds wanted to congratulate the crew while the men were at their deepest point. His voice went by radio to a ship on the surface and thence by underwater phone to *Aluminaut*. "Underwater telephone working exceptionally well," the log records. Mr. Reynolds himself said he heard the voices from the submarine "loud and clear."

Al Rutherford was chief engineer on the deepest dive. He wanted to go farther down. "I wish we had gone to the bottom," he told me. "As I remember, we were in about 9,000 feet of water. I always feel that if you are close to the bottom it's a shame to have to stop. I want to go to the bottom, photograph it, and see what's there. I'm an explorer, I guess. This business kindles the pioneer spirit, so to speak."

Aluminaut stayed at 6,250 feet for 33 minutes, then returned to the surface.

"Should I ever again," Professor Arronax wondered in *20,-000 Leagues*, "have such an opportunity of observing the wonders of the ocean?" That's what Jim Cooney wonders about his own trip upward from a mile and a quarter down. He did not have to rivet himself to his strain gauges. "I put my nose against the window," he said, "and watched the plankton. We had darkened the forward end of the ship. We had no lights."

The plankton put on a brilliant display of fireworks for the men aboard *Aluminaut*.

"I just can't describe the colors. They were like nothing we'd seen before," Cooney recalls. "Luminescent reds, yellows, greens, blues. The reds showed up closer, and the greens and blues further out."

The plankton joined together in colored strings in random shapes, Cooney said. "Anywhere from one inch to about one foot long. There were balls as small as a pack of cigarettes. There were spiral structures. That was about the major event of the trip."

"The thing that thrilled me," Al Rutherford said, "was that every quart of hydrospace was so full of life—plankton, egg chains, little shrimplike creatures called copepods, some fish."

Aluminaut returned to the surface with no difficulty. Then she was towed into her home port, Miami.

Wrote Jules Verne: "The great depths of the ocean are entirely unknown to us." But *Aluminaut*—and today's other deep-diving submarines—are changing that.

The Lifeless Depths

6

On the bottom of the sea nothing moved.

The ocean floor 3,000 feet down (almost three-fifths of a mile) had an eerie feeling.

No fish swam by.

No crabs scuttled across the floor.

No sharks prowled.

Outside the viewports of the submarine, nylon streamers, which ordinarily flutter to show the current, drooped lifeless. Even the water itself was dead still.

From inside *Deepstar 4000*, Dr. Eugene C. LaFond peered out. He and the two men with him were the first human beings to eyewitness a lifeless sea floor. "In all dives made with submersibles," says the Naval Undersea Warfare Center, San Diego—the former United States Navy Electronics Laboratory, which was operating *Deepstar 4000*—"this is the first time that such an area has been observed."

Dr. LaFond, who was head of the Marine Environment Division of the Navy Electronics Laboratory (NEL), had descended to the ocean bottom in *Deepstar* about ten miles north of Avalon, Santa Catalina Island, California. *Deepstar* made the dive December 4, 1966. That was Dr. LaFond's birthday anniversary. It would be one birthday he will never forget.

Only a few spots on the bottom of the ocean are believed to be without, or almost without, animal life of any kind—regions as devoid of life as the flaming craters and lava flows of volcanoes. There are such lifeless places on the sea floor in the Baltic Sea and in the Black Sea. Another, located by Dr. Robert J. Menzies, is at Cape Lookout Bight, 40 miles east of Morehead City, North Carolina. "Under twenty to thirty feet of bright blue seawater," Menzies says, "the bottom sediment is black, stinking, and poisonous." In the Mediterranean, there are spots that lack oxygen and therefore lack animals; there are others in the southern Adriatic, the Balearic, and the Aegean seas. The Gulf of Guinea on the west coast of Africa has lifeless depths. So does the coast of Venezuela. So do some of the deep Norwegian fjords, until winter storms churn up the depths and force new life-preserving oxygen into them.

All of these places are known because of photos by deep-sea cameras or the obtaining of samples of bottom water or by the evidences of dredges and net hauls. No man ever had reached a lifeless seabed before Dr. LaFond, Dale Good, the electronics (or instrumentation) engineer, and Bob Bradley of Westinghouse, the *Deepstar* pilot. They were at 33° 29.8′ North and 118° 22.1′ West.

It was what they did not see on the bottom that startled the three men:

No brittle stars—starfish with five to eight long, slender arms.

No sea cucumbers creeping over the bottom.

No gastropods—snail-like mollusks.

No crabs foraging on the remains of sea animals which have settled through the water columns.

All of these animals normally are present on the Pacific floor 3,000 feet down. We know this from photographed animals and their trails in the mud or sediment on the sea floor, and from earlier trips by deep-diving submersibles.

There were no fish in sight. No sablefish, in particular. The sable is a Pacific food fish related to the big-headed scorpaenidae. "It has a sharklike tail," Dr. LaFond told me. "The ones that we have seen off southern California vary from fifteen to fifty inches in length. The sablefish are very curious and come around the instruments on the brow of *Deepstar*. They come right up to the viewing port and look at you."

The sablefish, says the Navy, is virtually always to be seen near the bottom, in depths of 4,000 feet, off the coast.

The absence of the total animal population was what made the lifeless sea floor a haunting experience.

Dr. LaFond is a man who has spent almost his entire working life, since the 1930's, in oceanography. In September, 1934, he went as a research assistant to the Scripps Institution of Oceanography at San Diego State College, today the University of California at San Diego. "Scripps was," Dr. LaFond recalled to me, "about the only oceanographic place except the University of Washington and Woods Hole." At Scripps he found a young lady working as an oceanographic chemist. In 1935 they were married. "She took time off from oceanography," he says, "to raise two boys. Now, for the past five or six years, she has been working with me. We write joint papers. She was aboard the *Deepstar* tender, the *Burchtide*, when we made our dive to the lifeless sea floor."

Katherine LaFond at my request sent me a statement by her husband summarizing his reaction to the lifeless zone: "Of all the dives I have made over the past five years, this is the first time I have encountered an area really devoid of life. It is a truly eerie sensation. The sea floor at 3,000 feet normally contains a variety of life; brittle stars, sea cucumbers, fish, to name a few. In this San Pedro Basin area, though, the bottom showed only a layer of brown, flocculent material, with occasional dead organisms in various stages of decay to heighten the effect."

When Dr. LaFond and his companions noticed these dead organisms, it added to the feeling of cruising in haunted depths. They were sailing a few feet above a cemetery of sea creatures.

The most abundant were squid, in this case about 8 inches

long. There were 12 to 15 such corpses within two quarter-mile excursions over the sea floor.

The men saw a dead flatfish resembling a halibut, partly decomposed. They saw a few 'dead blackfish, each about a foot long. These they believed to be of the brotulid family. The brotulids, related to the blennies, are a family of deep-sea fish with big heads and long pointed tails and lateral-line systems. The lateral lines are rows of sense organs along their sides, so sensitive that a brotulid can detect currents caused by nearby creatures as they swim, feed, or even breathe.

A 6½-inch brotulid, *Bassogigas*, caught by the Danish surface research vessel *Galathea* in the Pacific's Sunda Deep in 1952, was brought up from 23,400 feet—the greatest depth at which a fish was ever caught. The previous depth record was that of another brotulid caught 19,800 feet down by Prince Albert of Monaco 50 years earlier.

Dr. LaFond, Bob Bradley, and Dale Good saw dead medusa-shaped jellyfish, with their multiple tentacles.

They saw, every once in a while, a beer can.

The dead fish and the dead squid, which were white, stood out in relief because they were outlined by a black border.

Fish must breathe by filtering oxygen out of the water through their gills. The black border around the dead squid and the dead fish suggested to Dr. LaFond that an oxygenless condition existed in the area.

"Nothing moved," reported the Navy. "This was in great contrast to the keen excitement felt on all other dives with submersibles."

The lifeless sea bottom was covered by a layer one centimeter thick of fine, brown organic matter. Samples were picked up by *Deepstar's* mechanical arms.

Even the water around *Deepstar* failed to move. "The water motion on the bottom," says Dr. LaFond, "was practically nil." It did not even stir up the finest particles. The men released fluorescein dye into the sea. It hung there; that is, it moved no faster than one/one-hundredth of a knot.

Deepstar returned to the surface, then dived to another spot on the bottom about six-tenths of a mile from the first location. She spent seven hours underwater noting the condition of the area. "These are the only two times," said Bradley, "in 187 dives in the *Deepstar* that we have found no living things." Both dives into the San Pedro Basin were into a 270-square-mile cup-shaped hollow on the bottom of the sea that shuts out the oxygen-carrying water from above it. "Just a big, stagnant basin," Dr. LaFond calls it.

Deepstar collected 15 samples of the water, which were analyzed by Phil Sloan. They showed the dissolved oxygen content of the water to be less than 0.1 milliliter of oxygen per liter of water.

This indicates, the Navy says, that normal fish and other bottom-dwelling animals cannot survive in the water. The dead organisms seen from *Deepstar* did not indicate a mass mortality, but only occasional, widely spaced dead organisms. The creatures probably swam into the area, the Navy says. They died and stayed where they fell among the remains of plankton from the upper levels of the sea, because nothing alive could come along and live long enough to devour their corpses.

This lifeless area seen by the three men aboard *Deepstar* has been called a Death Valley of the Deep and, by a Navy news service, a desert under the sea.

But was it a Death Valley? A desert? Even where nothing moved, there was at least one sign of life.

"There were," says the Navy, "some small worm tubes but no visible worms nor motion.

"The 1- or 2-centimeter-high tubes may have been created at some previous time or have been created by a species that required little or no oxygen."

In the Bay of Naples, for example, where there is a lack of oxygen on the bottom, the only known bottom animal is the worm *Spio fulginosus*. It lives in a tube.

There may be a little life—life that requires almost no oxygen—even in the supposedly lifeless areas on the bottom of the sea.

The "Deepstar" Monster

7

"Look, look!"

Pilot Joe Thompson of *Deepstar 4000* shouted the words.

Dr. LaFond stared through a viewport. The men were 4,000 feet down off California, on the bottom of the San Diego Trough, five miles from the Los Coronados Islands. They were southwest of San Diego, almost exactly on a line with the California-Mexico border.

Thompson at first saw a big cloud in the water. At least he saw something that took up a lot of space.

The big cloud approached.

It turned out to be a fish.

The fish was 30, maybe 40 feet long.

The fish swam right up to the window. "The eyes," Thompson says, "were as big as dinner plates. Then came the pectoral fin and finally the tail. I estimated the tail to be four to five feet high. The color of the fish was dark and mottled."

Deepstar, at the moment placing a current meter on the bottom with a mechanical arm, could not turn and follow the unknown creature.

What was it? Whatever it was, it was something neither Joe Thompson nor Dr. LaFond ever had seen before.

That is saying a great deal. Thompson is an experienced *Deepstar* pilot, familiar with the depths and bottom. Dr. La-Fond has traveled to the bottom of the sea not only in *Deepstar* but also as a scuba diver, in the bathyscaphe *Trieste*, and in the small Cousteau diving saucer, the *Soucoupe*. He has made 49 cruises to study the Indian Ocean. He told me himself of the big fish on the bottom of the sea.

"You won't believe this," he said, "but a fish that might have been forty feet long came up and looked at us. His tail was something like a grouper-type tail. Yet I can't believe it was a grouper. It was much too big."

I had met Dr. LaFond at the Columbia University Club in New York City; on its walls are several mounted fish caught by Columbia men. The longest is about 6 feet.

A 30-foot-long fish would be possible on the bottom of the Pacific; a 40-foot-long fish would be startling indeed. That is shown by the figures I found when I looked up the records. "The biggest fish ever caught," says Boris Arnov, Jr., in *Oceans of the World*, "was not a true fish but a whale shark. Taken in the Florida keys in 1912, it measured 38 feet in length and its weight was estimated at 26,594 pounds." Dr. LaFond did not think this fish was a shark. The whale shark, which feeds on plankton, is presumably restricted to the surface anyway.

The largest fishes include the sawfish, says Osmond P. Breland in *Animal Life and Lore*. Dr. Breland, a University of Texas zoology professor who keeps records on the animal kingdom, says sawfish often are over 20 feet, and one reaching 29 has been reported. "Individuals of thirty feet or more are sometimes encountered," say J. R. Norman and F. C. Fraser in *Giant Fishes, Whales and Dolphins*.

"Of the game fishes," says Boris Arnov, "the broadbill swordfish grows to the largest size, reaching a length of twenty feet and a weight of more than one thousand pounds."

Other large fishes in the ocean include the largest sunfish

(an almost circular, disk-shaped creature) on record, 10 feet 2 inches long; the black marlin, 14 feet 8 inches; the striped marlin, 13 feet 5 inches; the blue marlin, 12 feet 10½ inches; the sailfish, 10 feet 6½ inches; the bluefin tuna, 9 feet 8 inches; the tarpon, 7 feet 5½ inches; the barracuda, 8 feet or more. Ocean sturgeon, 12 to 14 feet long, and one 26 feet long, have been reported.

The ribbonfish, which looks more like a ribbon than a fish, has been taken over 20 feet in length. From shipboard off the coast of New Jersey, Dr. Lionel A. Walford, director of the Sandy Hook Marine Laboratories of the Bureau of Sport Fisheries and Wildlife, saw a 40- to 50-foot transparent ribbon-like creature. "It looked like so much jelly," he said. It was identified as a ribbonfish, or oarfish. "Ours," said Dr. Walford, "was at least ten feet longer than the largest specimen recorded."

What these figures mean is that a true fish 40 feet long would be a whopper—the tallest fisherman's tale of all time.

Thompson, though, feels he had a good look at his fish. "It was coming right down the port, or pilot's, side of the submarine," he said. "I guessed its length. But we had stuck instruments into the bottom. You know how far apart your instruments are. Things do look bigger beneath the surface. But that fish kept swimming and swimming."

Dr. LaFond and Thompson at first hesitated to say anything about it because "nobody would believe us."

Then another venerable oceanographic institution on the California coast, Scripps, discovered a deep-sea monster of its own. Scripps thought its monster also was of a size and type not known in California waters.

What happened was this: Scripps people, working under Professor John D. Isaacs, director of marine life research, were photographing marine life at the bottom near the Los Coronados Islands—near where LaFond and Thompson saw their big fish.

To do it, the Scripps researchers heave overboard an unmanned robot device. The robot contains a camera that takes a picture every 15 minutes on the bottom. After a while, the robot drops some weights and the robot and camera ascend to the surface, where they are picked up by a surface ship.

Three times the robot camera device, which had been developed by Professor Isaacs, George Schick, and Meredith Sessions of Scripps, was dropped into the sea.

On two out of the three trips to 6,000 feet down, its pictures showed the large, shadowy, dark body of an unknown monster. The strange creature appeared about 25 feet long. Scripps at first thought it had encountered an unknown sea beast in the California Pacific.

Then Carl Hubbs, Scripps professor of marine biology, identified it tentatively as the Greenland, or sleeper, shark.

The brown-to-black Greenland, or sleeper, shark, *Somniosus microcephalus*, is known to exist near Greenland and Labrador, but practically everything else about it is unknown. It lives in cold water, far from most shipping lanes and pretty much out of touch with men, and only sometimes strays to Cape Cod. It had not been known, or suspected, off southern California. The Pacific where it was found is warm on the surface and cold at the depths. The Greenland shark might like the temperature at 6,000 feet.

The Greenland shark's maximum reported length, the Bureau of Sport Fisheries and Wildlife says, is 21 feet. Its size at birth is unknown.

"There must be a lot of them out there," said Carl Hubbs, "or we wouldn't have gotten two photographs in only three drops." He still is not sure what the pictures show: "We can't be absolutely certain till we go out and catch one."

To go out and catch one is exactly what Professor Isaacs intends to do.

The monster, he believes, may live on large animals that die on the surface and sink to the bottom. "I want to increase the bait," he says, "until we're using as much as ten tons in one piece. Then we'll put a camera above it and see what happens. We will probably use dead horses for bait, though we may kill sharks on the surface and use them." It will be hard to get a ten-ton piece of anything except a whale. Then he hopes to hook and bring to the surface the Greenland shark or whatever it proves to be.

In the meantime, Isaacs and Brown have photographed two very large sharks on the deep bottom at over a mile down off Hawaii. These were definitely, Professor Isaacs tells me, *not* the Greenland shark. Dr. LaFond and Joe Thompson, when they saw photos of the Scripps Institution's sea monsters, dug out their magnetic tape recordings of the descriptions they had made at 4,000 feet in *Deepstar*, decided to tell their big fish story, and did so. After Dr. LaFond recounted it to me, I in turn told him the story Art Markel, the *Aluminaut* manager, had told me: that Markel had seen a complete fifteenth-century galleon on the bottom of the sea off Spain. Dr. LaFond, who had begun his own tale of a 40-foot-long fish with the words, "You won't believe this," had a quick comment on Art Markel's story:

"I don't believe that."

The Riddle
of the Trench

8

As Bob Menzies of Duke University cruised almost four miles above the floor of the Milne-Edwards Deep of the Pacific's Peru-Chile Trench, he tried, with his deep-sea cameras, to solve some of the mysteries of the trench. Some of his photographs, instead, created a new riddle of the seas.

Aboard the *Anton Bruun* a specially-built apparatus lowered cameras, at the ends of steel cable, to as far as 18,000 feet down.

One day, about 20 miles from the island of Hormigas de Afuera, Dr. Menzies, who is now at Florida State University, and his scientists lowered their cameras to a point about 6,000 feet beneath the sea, on the side of the Milne-Edwards Deep.

Sonar aboard the *Anton Bruun* had indicated some strange shapes on the side of the trench. The shapes did not seem to belong there. So the cameras went down to take photos. They were hauled up. The job took hours. The pictures were developed.

They showed—what?

They showed what appear to be columns. Carved rock columns.

With a Lamont 35-millimeter multishot underwater camera, Dr. Menzies took a total of about 1,000 photographs. Most clearly showed mud strewn with animal tracks and remains. But some clearly showed what seems to be jointed rock.

One picture showed pillars standing upright—extending four feet out of the mud. Other pictures showed rocks that look like pillars that have fallen over.

When Dr. Menzies tried again to locate and again to photograph the upright columns, he failed to find them. This is understandable: A change in bottom currents alone could have swept his camera away from the spot. Instead, he found more fallen pillars. Some of the pillars appear to have some kind of writing on them.

The numbers three and nine seem to show up on some of the lying-down pillars, but these could be tracings made by marine animals. Even so, Dr. Menzies thought these tracings unusual. But, he said, "it is almost beyond belief to consider that the inscriptions represent man-made inscriptions."

"We did not find these structures elsewhere," Dr. Menzies said. "Elsewhere, the bottom is mud, as would be expected."

The ship's sonar showed other irregularities in the topography of the ocean floor in the same area.

"It seems incredulous, the idea of a sunken city," Dr. Menzies comments.

But not impossible. We already know of other sunken cities.

"Today," says *Seas, Maps, and Men*, "about half of the three hundred major ports and coastal cities built between 3000 B.C. and the fall of the Roman Empire are submerged and many are being excavated by underwater archaeologists."

These are Mediterranean Sea cities. Bob Menzies' findings were made in the Pacific off the coast of Callao, the port of Lima, capital of Peru. No city beneath the waves was even suspected here. But nearby, on land, are some aged Inca ruins. Some scientists believe that there were civilizations here thousands of years before the Incas.

Some scientists believe that the land hereabouts is slowly sinking, as the land that forms the side of the Milne-Edwards

Deep, where the columns were photographed, might have done. Also, there are active volcanoes in the area. And earthquakes occur here. They might have caused a city to sink.

Eyewitnesses inside the Milne-Edwards Deep could clear up the mystery of just what the cameras pictured. Bob Menzies would like to dive to the site himself. He would like to do so in either *Aluminaut, Deep Quest*, or in the *Alvin*, all of which could reach the mysterious columns.

In *20,000 Leagues Under the Sea*, the *Nautilus* carries her people to the sunken ruins of the legendary Atlantis, the lost civilization of the ancients.

Atlantis has been discussed by men for 3,000 years at least. The ancient Greek, Plato, tells in his dialogues of the high level of civilization in Atlantis, until Atlantis was destroyed by an earthquake.

Atlantis was, supposedly, an island in the western Atlantic. It was shown on maps until about the middle of the eighteenth century. By then, no one having rediscovered it, mapmakers gave up and dropped it.

Plato's Atlantis may have been discovered. In 1966, J. W. Mavor, Jr., of Woods Hole, who had helped develop the *Alvin*, and Professor A. G. Galanopoulos of the University of Athens, suggested that the island of Thira, near Crete, in the Mediterranean, was the original Atlantis. Thira was destroyed by a volcanic eruption around 3,400 years ago. The roar of the eruption may have been heard as far away as Scandinavia. What may be ruins plus traces of Minoan civilization have been found both ashore and beneath the sea near Thira. Mr. Mavor wants *Alvin* to dive around Thira.

Before the cruise of the *Anton Bruun* in 1966, no one imagined there might be a lost civilization over one mile down in the Pacific. If so, it will be by far the deepest archaeological discovery ever made.

If he reads a copy of *20,000 Leagues Under the Sea*, Bob Menzies may find—and dream over—this passage: "For one instant," said Professor Arronax, as the *Nautilus* was cruising under the sea near the Straits of Gibraltar, "I caught a glimpse

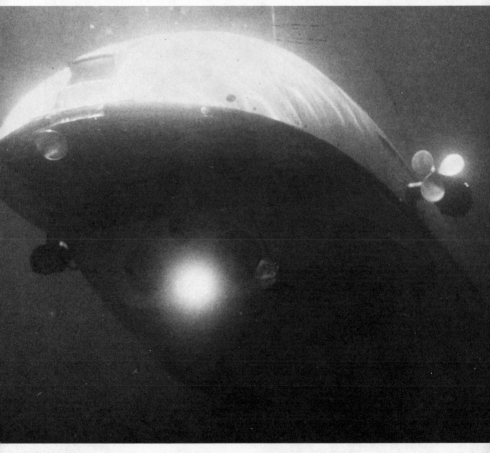

Journeys to the bottom of the sea. For the first time in history, today deep-diving submarines take men to deep-ocean floor to see what's there. Deepstar 4000 *explores Pacific, Atlantic, Gulf of Mexico.*

On bottom of Pacific Ocean, Deepstar 4000 (background) carries first men ever to witness an oxygen-poor area where nothing can live. They see only dead animals. Sticking up: temperature probe.

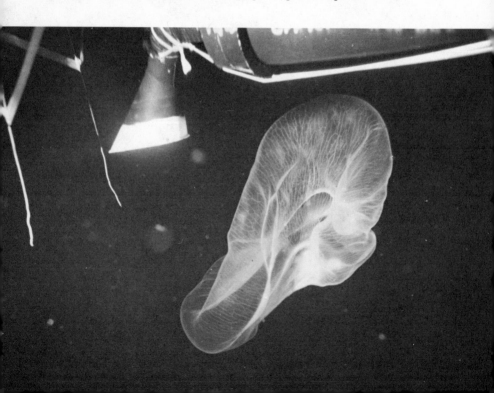

With floodlights, Pilot Joe Thompson of Deepstar 4000 *thought he saw a 40-foot-long fish, bigger than any known. On nearby sea floor, Scripps Institution photographed this monster, possibly a rare Greenland shark.*

First unknown animal to be captured by a deep-diving submarine is shown just before being picked up by Deepstar 4000. *A medusa, it has been named* Deepstaria enigmatica. *Dr. Eric Barham caught it October 10, 1966.*

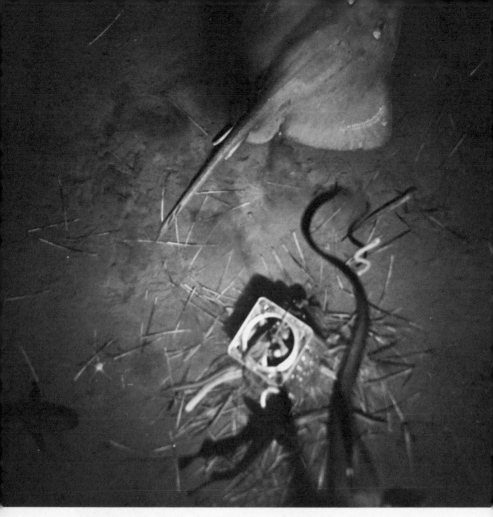

6,000 feet down, near where Deepstar 4000 *encountered 40-foot-long fish, Scripps photographed grenadier rattails and a skate (around can of bait). Many fish of the ocean abyss have big heads and long stringy tails.*

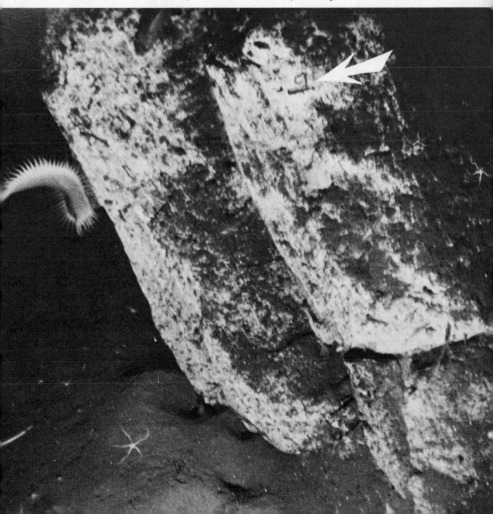

A lost civilization? This photograph of what look like man-made columns was taken 6000 feet down off Peru, on November 29, 1965. Robert J. Menzies lowered camera from aboard the surface ship Anton Bruun.

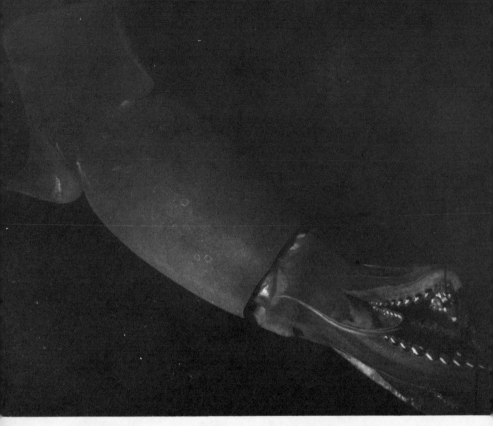

Big squid, a ten-armed marine monster, takes own photo. Squid is off Peru, in Milne-Edwards trench. Camera was Bob Menzies'. In the trench, Menzies found many animals, including 53 new species of crustaceans.

Minerals cover bottom of deep sea in some areas. Manganese nodules, here, are one of seabed resources that may be tapped. Aluminaut found manganese nodules and manganese pavement on Atlantic bottom off Georgia.

A crab appears hostile. Photograph was made through viewport of Aluminaut on bottom of Atlantic. Aluminaut is deepest-diving of the new submarines. She can reach 15,000 feet down, 75 percent of ocean floor.

*Almost four miles down: Photo of Marianas Trench from bathyscaphe
Trieste, in Pacific near Guam, shows one of deepest seabeds ever seen.
U.S. Navy's future 20,000-foot-deep submarines will reach this realm.*

*Brittle Star is one of most common animals to welcome men to bottom
of deep sea. This is a scene viewed from the Trieste. Starfish dwell in
shallow water just offshore, also live at many depths beneath the surface.*

of the beautiful ruins of the temple of Hercules, buried in the ground, according to Pliny, and with the low island which supports it."

As he today ponders his startling photos of the columns on the bottom of the sea, Bob Menzies wonders. "Maybe," he says, "the idea of a sunken civilization is not so incredulous after all. Someday I will go back there."

Dive 176 for "Star II"

9

I was chasing a crab scuttling across the bottom. From about a foot above, I watched it through a round viewing port located right between my feet in the research submarine. I had to speed up the submarine to keep up.

I moved forward two gearshift-like knobs atop levers that stuck out of a black box, or console, that was resting on my right knee. The console was connected by electric cable to the bulkhead of the submarine, and the console could be passed back and forth between the pilot and me so that either one of us could control the submersible.

The submarine, *Star II*, gathered speed as I pursued the crab. Soon we were traveling at the boat's full speed, 3½ knots. That's a man's walking speed. But when you're 6 to 12 inches above the floor of the sea, the bottom goes by like a blur.

In a few seconds, we caught up with the crab. I pulled the knobs back to what would be neutral on a gearshift auto. *Star II* stopped almost instantly. That's a characteristic of deep-diving submarines.

We were just above the crab. We had a closeup look. To-day's deep-diving subs can take you right up to and just a few inches from creatures on the bottom of the sea. That's another characteristic of deep-diving submarines. Only individual scuba divers get closer looks, and they cannot go nearly so deep. *Star II* can go 1,200 feet down. No scuba or other diver ever has dived that far.

Still another characteristic of the deepwater exploring craft is that many of them are easy to learn to drive, or pilot.

Ten minutes before seeing the crab I had never controlled one of the new boats. I had gone down with Bob Hill, the pilot, on what was Dive 176 for *Star II*. We were in Fishers Island Sound, near the eastern (Atlantic) entrance to Long Island Sound, past which Jules Verne's *Nautilus* cruised. Hill had been holding the black box, and he had spent a few minutes showing me the two knobs, one controlling each two-horsepower electric motor and propeller on *Star II*, and the knobs' positions. You push the knobs forward, to go forward; backward to move the boat backward. When the knobs are in neutral, the boat stands still.

To turn, Hill explained, you push one of the knobs forward and pull the other back. I tried it. I watched the bottom as I did so. The little submarine spun like a ballet dancer twirling on a toe.

The only other control is at the right side of the console, a lever that sticks out. It controls *Star II's* hovering propeller, or vertical thruster, overhead. You push it forward to go up, pull it backward to descend.

I quickly knew how to make the *Star II* go forward, back-ward, speed up, slow down, stop, stand still, and go up or down in the sea. All this had taken about five minutes.

As I was on my first ride in a deep-diving submarine, I was as startled as anyone when Hill placed the console on my knee and said:

"Here, you take her for a while."

I did. The crab came along, Bob pointed out the crab, and I chased it.

I managed to bounce the submarine off the bottom a couple of times. There was no harm done. *Star II* has beneath her hull runners like sled runners to sit on the sea floor. They make her bounces softer.

But I felt complete confidence in my ability to control the *Star II*. I felt sure that I could surface her and get her back to her mother ship, if necessary. No fear. No sweat. Simplicity of operation: This characteristic of many of the latest deep-diving boats is a big reason why you and I and anyone else can drive his own submarine. It is a big reason why future journeys to the bottom of the sea are going to be made not just by highly skilled specialists, like the Navy's hydronauts, but by people from all walks of life.

I became a pilot of *Star II*—and I have a card in my wallet, a blazer badge, and a tie pin to prove it—because I was invited to come up to New London and Groton, Connecticut, and have a look at her.

Off Groton, a big launch, a kind used by offshore oilmen for transportation, took us several miles across Fishers Island Sound to *Star II's* mother ship, a powered offshore-oil supply barge named *Gemini*. The *Gemini's* home port is Houston, Texas, and she was flying the blue-and-white house flag of her Houston owners, Astro Marine. Both the company and *Gemini* herself are named in honor of the astronauts who train in the Manned Spacecraft Center near Houston.

From *Gemini*, an outboard motorboat, a Boston whaler, took me across the last few hundred yards of salt water to *Star II*.

The submarine did not look very large. She was trailing a bright orange buoy that, when she submerged, would show the men aboard *Gemini* where she was at all times. The buoy looked almost as big as *Star II*. She is a small submarine actually: 17 feet 9½ inches long, the length of a car or a living room.

She weighs five tons afloat. She is international orange (to be seen easily beneath the surface) and white (to be seen easily on the surface).

I scrambled from the Boston whaler over the rim of the fairwater, or conning tower, of *Star II*. Both the whaler and *Star II* were gently bobbing on the sea.

I saw what I had to do next: lower myself through the open circular hatch. To do this I had to put my weight on my arms and hands on the rim of the hatch. I did.

Then I discovered the hatch was so narrow I could not see where I was going. I was poking my feet down into the space beneath without being able to see them at all.

"I'll guide you," a voice called. Bob Hill took my feet and placed them on the copilot's seat on the port side.

Then I got the rest of the way into the submarine and introduced myself.

Robert G. Hill, 32, of Norwich, Connecticut, is a machinist. He helped build *Star II*, knows every mechanical part in her, and is an experienced pilot of her and other Star boats of General Dynamics.

"I've driven *Star I* and *Asherah*," he recalls, "around Fishers Island Sound and Block Island Sound. The little *Star I* could dive only to two hundred feet, and was used for looking underneath ships' bottoms and at keels. We tested a fuel cell in it." But *Star II* is his baby: "I have made close to eighty to ninety dives in her."

"Topside, Topside," he said, into the underwater phone to men aboard *Gemini*. "*Star II*. *Star II*. Request permission to dive."

"Permission granted," the answer came back. The underwater phone's range, Hill told me, is about 5,000 feet.

He opened the main ballast tank, took in water, and we started down.

The depth recorder, a dial in front of me with a single pointer, showed our increasing depth. In front of Hill, a dial full of flashing red gleams showed him how far above the bottom we were at all times.

I was getting a look beneath the surface. The water at first was light, or whitish. It was just like flying in an airplane through a light gray cloud.

I was not prepared for what I saw next: the plankton.

I had of course for years read about the plankton—the tiny animals and plants of the sea. I was gazing at the light water through the port just over my left ear. The water was filled with black specks, tinier than the point of a pin.

What looked like billions and billions of these tiny black specks filled the port and all the water as far out as I could see. They all seemed to keep their distance, a fraction of an inch, from each other. They did not seem to be moving—in any direction, or up, or down. I knew at once they were not silt. I had never seen anything like them before.

"What," I asked Bob, "is this?" He grinned.

"The plankton," he replied.

The plankton animals that can be seen with your eyes are the macroplankton. The rest you can see only through a microscope, if then: Some of the plankton animals are so tiny not even an electron microscope can make them clearly visible. The nannoplankton may be one-ten-thousandth of an inch in size. The most abundant creatures or plants in the sea, especially on the bottom, are so very small they escape through the meshes of a plankton net. They are the bacteria.

I saw at about this moment some grayish specks amid the dark ones. This is the so-called "sea snow"—dead or waste matter from the animals and plants of the plankton that floats downward in the sea and furnishes nourishment to living animals and plants.

You don't see the plankton on the surface: The sea looks like empty dark water from there. Just beneath the surface in *Star II* you see that the light water teems with incredible amounts of life. To realize that all these tiny specks, which you can barely see, are all living creatures is a fact that the mind finds difficult to comprehend.

But there it was, just outside the viewport, just beyond my left ear. A deep-diving submarine like *Star II* takes you into a new world.

Star II and the other new small research subs are a new kind of vehicle. They move, and you feel it, usually gently—but not like a car, train, plane, motorboat, or ship. It is a different motion from any you are accustomed to. It is slow motion; for the most part, movement beneath the sea, like the rippling motion of a fish, is—or appears to be—slow.

We sank toward the bottom. A few feet above it, I saw it: gray mud in Long Island Sound. Nothing spectacular. It wasn't very deep where we were.

But, I thought, here I am. Here I am, not a sailor, but a civilian in ordinary dacron-and-wool business trousers and blue cotton shirt, sitting right here. In a pretty soft (foam rubber) seat, at that.

On the bottom of the sea.

Hill turned on *Star II's* powerful lights that flood the sea with illumination. I could see everything better.

I saw a flatfish buried in the silt.

I saw a round sea urchin (I thought).

I saw clams in the mud. I was impressed by the amount of life, or signs of life, on the floor of Fishers Island Sound. The bottom crawled with living creatures. Everywhere too were shells or parts of animals that had once been alive.

I saw a mound with a round tubular hole in its top—the house of some bottom-dwelling animal. A fish swam by, with the fluid, slow, rippling motion of the world beneath the sea.

Hill then proceeded to give me my five-minute course in piloting *Star II*.

"There's a current here," he said. "We can drift with it, the way Jacques Piccard plans to do for weeks beneath the Gulf Stream. Please put the knobs in neutral." I did.

The current, three-quarters of a knot, moved us backward

and sideways. That was an ideal speed for seeing things on the bottom.

I saw live clams and dead clams and many kinds of shells and seaweed. Then some strange straight marks on the sand. I thought they might be tracks of some mysterious animal that lived there. I brought the submarine back to show them to Hill. He smiled.

"Our own tracks," he said. "The submarine makes those marks with her runners when she hits or sits on the bottom."

"The *Nautilus*," wrote Jules Verne, "floated in the midst of a phosphorescent bed, which, in this obscurity, became quite dazzling. It was produced by myriads of luminous animalculae. . . . There was unusual life and vigour; this was truly living light!"

Hill told me of a scene like that he had actually witnessed: "*Star II* dived to eight hundred feet off Nassau in the Bahamas. I switched off the lights. The whole sea became alive with luminescence, glowing animals. No colors, just a white fluorescent light, filling the sea the way Fourth of July fireworks fill the sky. Once we could not see out of our ports, so many fish were jammed against them."

Star II can keep her pilot and another man—copilot, scientist, or guest—alive for 48 hours. That is, they are provided breatheable air for that long.

Hill reached for the mouthpiece of the underwater telephone, at the end of a wire running to a hook on the forward bulkhead.

"*Star II, Star II*," he said, "calling Topside. We are about to check the atmosphere."

"Topside to *Star II*," the voice from the underwater phone announced, loud and clear. "Go ahead." The voice came through a squawk box, or loudspeaker, instead of through a telephone earphone.

Hill squeezed a rubber bulb a few times and got it full of the air we were breathing. He squirted the air into a glass device containing a chemical that tested for CO_2 (carbon dioxide), the poison that men exhale. The test showed we were OK as far as CO_2 was concerned.

A similar test for oxygen showed we needed some. Hill turned a valve, and a canister full of oxygen under pressure squirted into the air.

The air at once seemed fresher.

Hill reported his results to the men aboard *Gemini*.

"Topside calling *Star II*," the underwater phone said next, "there is a sailing ship over you. Do not come to the surface."

"Roger," Hill replied. We stayed down. Moments later, *Gemini* told us the sailing ship had moved away.

I realized how impressed I had been with the competent way the *Gemini* crew and the *Star II* people functioned—pilots like Hill and Al Rutherford; Samuel L. Fiske, operations manager; and Robert McGratten, General Dynamics' manager of Underwater Development Engineering. They were all young men. They wore sport shirts, shorts or slacks, dark glasses, and suntans. Literate, highly skilled, they knew, and were fond of, what they were doing. While one of them takes *Star II* down, others watch from *Gemini's* bridge or man the underwater phone aboard *Gemini*. Watching them in action is like watching a championship football team.

"Let me show you something," Hill said. As we sat on the bottom, he switched off the motors. For a moment silence fell —deep, utter silence of a kind you rarely experience. All was "still as death," as Jules Verne once described the depths.

Then the sounds of the sea began to come through to us —sounds magnified somewhat by our sonar.

I could hear the click, click or snap, snap of some shrimp or fish talking, or at least making noises. I could actually hear the sand being moved along the bottom. I knew the depths of the sea are not quiet.

Hill asked *Gemini* for permission to surface. It was granted. He blew out the auxiliary ballast tank. Through the viewport just beneath my feet, the sea floor fell away. We came up quickly. *Star II* can ascend or descend 50 feet a minute.

At the surface, the viewing ports are still under water, so we could not tell when we reached the top. "Topside, Topside," said the underwater phone, "to *Star II*. You are on the surface and the whaler is standing by."

At this point, the conning tower over our heads was still full of water. Bob Hill pointed the bow of *Star II* slightly down to let the water drain out.

He opened the hatch. I lifted myself out through it with my arms alone. (A simpler way to get out I learned, too late to do me any good, is to stand on the pilot's shoulders.) I scrambled into the whaler. My trip in *Star II*, which had lasted about an hour (about 40 minutes on the bottom), was over. Its effects are lasting indefinitely: The bottom of the sea as it rolled along beneath my feet and before my eyes, and the myriads and myriads of teeming plankton, at eye level, just beyond my left ear, I can see right now.

The Bus
to the Bottom

10

The first submarine in the world to take you to the bottom of the sea and let you step out and walk around there is the Perry-Link *Deep Diver*.

Men inside *Deep Diver*, looking out through viewports, can search and explore the ocean floor. What makes *Deep Diver* different is that divers can leave her, move onto the ocean floor, and themselves roam and work there on the bottom.

Deep Diver can cruise along above a sea-bottom cable or pipeline as men inside her inspect it. Then, when a break in the cable or pipeline is spotted, *Deep Diver's* aquanauts or frogmen can step outside into the sea and repair the break.

A preview of *Deep Diver* was given 100 years ago by Jules Verne. In his book, Captain Nemo, Professor Arronax, and others stepped out of the *Nautilus* on the bottom. They wore tanks of breathing air on their backs, like knapsacks, and like the tanks carried on the backs of today's scuba divers. They walked on the bottom, then returned aboard the *Nautilus*. Says Professor Arronax: "I returned to my room, in great wonder at this surprising excursion at the bottom of the sea."

Navy frogmen for years have been able to leave submarines submerged at shallow depths. *Deep Diver* has put men on the bottom 700 feet down and theoretically can put men at any depth to 1,350 feet. So far, both British and American divers have worked well at 600 and 700 feet, but no deeper.

To be able to leave *Deep Diver* on the bottom pleases A. C. "Chet" Smith, the Naval Academy ('34) graduate who spent 12 years in submarines with the Navy and now is president of Ocean Systems, Incorporated, which operates *Deep Diver*. Of submarines and the sea, he says: "Being inside a cigar is not the same as being out in the ocean—becoming 'part of it.'

"*Deep Diver* is an important new concept because it's less of a problem to work effectively from a submarine than it is to dive from air into water."

Until *Deep Diver* cruised the seas, a human diver had to go over the side of a ship on the surface. "The real problem of a diver," Smith said to me, "is the interface between air and water." Whether the diver is in a scuba outfit, the old hard-hat gear (with air lines all the way from bottom to surface), or even in a diving bell, he encounters problems entering the sea through its surface. Rough weather is one of them. Many dives are canceled because of heavy seas on the surface—possibly hundreds of feet above where the work of the divers will be done. There may be quiet water on the sea floor where their task lies. Other dives are canceled because of strong currents at the surface. These things a diver aboard *Deep Diver* cruises right through. He gets a free journey to the bottom of the sea. Then, when he reaches the sea floor, he steps right out, perfectly fresh and ready to go to work. "If he gets in trouble on the bottom—if his face mask leaks, for instance," Smith said, "he can step right in again. He does not have the long climb to the surface seeking help. He just has to step inside the submarine.

"We take the diver through the interface of air and water —the surface," Smith says. "On the bottom, we take him close to the place where he is going to work. We pressurize a compartment in the submarine. It takes three minutes. We open the hatch. The diver stands on the bottom. He has reached it in perfect comfort. He is fresh and rested. He does his job on the bottom. When he is through, and at this point he is tired and cold, he just ducks into the submarine.

"From a mobile point of view, *Deep Diver* opens new avenues of travel. *Deep Diver* is not an ordinary submarine. She is a diver transport vehicle—a method to get people down to work efficiently underwater."

Deep Diver is the brainchild of—the more technical phrase is "conceived, designed, and engineered by"—Edwin Albert Link, today the chief marine consultant of Ocean Systems. She was built at Perry Submarine Builders, Incorporated, of West Palm Beach, Florida.

Ed Link, born in 1904, is the man who conceived and built devices that never leave solid earth yet simulate flying. These are called Link Aviation Trainers. Hundreds of thousands of Americans, especially during World War II, have gone through a Link trainer period to become pilots.

Having done a considerable amount of work to conquer the air, Ed Link turned to the ocean. Here his goal constantly has been, as it is in the case of *Deep Diver*, to put men on the bottom in such a way that they can stay there for long periods and work there efficiently.

He has done this with two of the world's most skillful divers: Bob Stenuit, a Belgian, and Jon Morrow Lindbergh, the son of aviator Charles A. Lindbergh and Anne Morrow Lindbergh. Charles Lindbergh, who became a pilot when planes were simpler than now and Link trainers had not been invented, in 1927 became the first man in history to fly a heavier-than-air craft nonstop across the Atlantic Ocean, from New York City to Paris. The monoplane he flew was the *Spirit of St. Louis.* His son has turned to the sea.

Jon Lindbergh told me how he got into oceanography. I met him at the Cosmos Club, a gathering spot for scientists, explorers, and other out-of-the-ordinary citizens in Washington, D.C. He had been a student at Stanford University in

California, he said. "Then in 1952," he went on, "I sailed on a cruise of the *Kevin Moran*." The *Kevin Moran* is an ocean-going tug that belongs to the Moran Tugboat Company, most of whose tugs stay inside New York harbor, crisscross it hauling barges, and dock incoming ships. On the *Kevin Moran*, said Lindbergh, "We went to Newfoundland, the Grand Banks, Recife in Brazil, the Azores, Dakar in Africa."

The *Kevin Moran* was making an oceanographic cruise—sampling the rocks and sediment on the bottom by means of deep-sea trawls and corers. She was doing work for Columbia University scientists, including Dr. Maurice Ewing. Dr. Ewing has turned out many of today's young oceanographers. "Doc Ewing was the power behind the cruise," Lindbergh remembers. "He was right there."

Lindbergh did his military service in the Navy. There he started diving, in the middle 1950's, and he has been diving ever since. After joining forces with Ed Link, Lindbergh dived with Bob Stenuit to set a record under water that is comparable to his father's achievement in flying from New York to Paris.

From June 30 to July 2, 1964, Lindbergh and Stenuit, as a team of two men, made the longest (49 hours) deep (432 feet) dive ever performed. They did it near Nassau, in the Bahamas, in the Atlantic.

Lindbergh lived during the dive, he said later, "in a little house on the bottom of the sea." The little house was designed by Ed Link. It was inflatable, like an inflatable life raft—and it was full inside of breathing gas (oxygen, helium, nitrogen) kept at the same pressure as the pressure of the surrounding water. The little house on the bottom of the sea was called the SPID (*S*ubmersible *P*ortable *I*nflatable *D*welling).

Lindbergh and Stenuit were lowered to SPID in a steel diving chamber. The diving chamber also was full of the breathing gas at the same pressure as that of the water at the 432-foot depth where the men would crawl out of the bottom of the chamber and paddle over to the SPID. This pressurizing of the breathing gas acclimatizes the divers at the depths.

Lindbergh and Stenuit found that cans of foods inside SPID, unpressurized in any way, were squashed by the pressure, but that the food inside was edible. "On tonight's menu," said Stenuit, "carrot juice and corned beef, canned water, fruit salad." The two men on the bottom of the sea watched sardines dance a ballet. They gazed upward at king mackerels, jacks, and barracudas "all twisting and turning tirelessly." They saw what Stenuit called "a huge big silhouette." It was "only a peaceful grouper (a big fish) which nibbles on our garbage and on some spoiled ham which we have thrown in the water. It was as big as a boar; it must weigh two hundred pounds." Stenuit found other creatures on the sea floor: "When I put my mask close enough to the coarse sandy bottom I can see it is teeming with life, sponges, worms, minute royal blue fluorescent fish I would like to bring back to make into a ring or earrings. Chunks of dead coral, scattered all about on the bottom, swarm like beehives with little flabby creatures. Sometimes, from the far end of a hole, a big round, yellow eye looks at you."

Jon Lindbergh wrote a note to his children from the bottom of the sea: "Through the window of SPID, I see thousands of silverfish, and a big grouper follows me on my walks like a poodle."

Later, the great grouper tried to squeeze into SPID through the round entrance hole in the bottom that serves as a front door. The big fish got stuck in the door. Ten times in one night the grouper crashed into SPID. When Stenuit took pictures with flashlights, he attracted six other groupers that pushed him around.

The next day, Lindbergh and Stenuit could see 150 feet straight out and 150 feet up. After spending 49 hours at 432 feet down, they were hauled up inside their diving bell, were decompressed (slowly, over 92 hours), and carried into Miami aboard Ed Link's surface ocean-exploring ship, *Sea Diver*.

Man's longest deep dive—or man's deepest long dive—had ended.

Joseph B. MacInnis, 39, a Canadian from Toronto, who is

a diver himself and is Lindbergh and Stenuit's doctor, has commented on what the dive means. He listed the problems: helium voice distortion (sound travels three times as fast in helium as in air, so voices sound like Donald Duck); the need for more breathing gas to support muscular work; and the difficulty of controlling humidity in an atmosphere in direct contact with the sea (both Lindbergh and Stenuit complained of softened skin and rashes). Both men were cold. "In the water," said Dr. MacInnis, "we realized heated suits are required to keep divers comfortable even in the Caribbean Sea." As he came up, Stenuit complained of a "sawdust feeling" in his fingers that seemed to progress toward his wrists. "Decompression sickness is so diverse," said Dr. MacInnis, "that almost any symptom has to be taken seriously."

Dr. MacInnis listed the positive results of the dive: It showed the way divers can stay down and work upon the continental shelf, generally 600 feet or less in depth. The men were completely saturated with 20 atmospheres of helium, MacInnis pointed out, and they could have stayed down 49 days as well as 49 hours. "There do not, then," he concludes, "seem to be any physiological or psychological barriers that will prevent the occupation of any part of the continental shelf . . . at this point, the gates of the deep shelf have been opened."

You may have seen Lindbergh and Stenuit on TV. Walter Cronkite, the University of Texas alumnus who telecasts news for CBS, showed *Deep Diver* diving near Grand Bahama Island in the Caribbean on his TV show, "The 21st Century," in 1967. He interviewed Lindbergh and Stenuit. Cronkite himself went down aboard *Deep Diver* and showed SPID on the bottom. He called this particular program "The Deep Frontier," and presented *Deep Diver* as the first of a series of lock-out, lock-in diver submarines that would make development of the ocean floor possible. Cronkite himself locked out and stepped out of *Deep Diver* and walked the ocean floor 80 feet beneath the surface.

"To go down in the submarine and lock out on the bottom," Cronkite said in New York City much later, "required for me a minimum of skill. We went down and swam around." He was impressed with the fact that *Deep Diver* can take down a man—and the man does not need long years of training as a diver to roam the bottom of the sea.

Chet Smith, the president of Ocean Systems, dived down and met Cronkite on the bottom. "A real experience," Smith called it. "Later on," Smith said, "it was a cinch for me to go down and lock in and lock out."

Another place you may have seen *Deep Diver* was in a 1967 issue of *Life*. *Life* showed the submarine on the bottom, as her divers prowled the sea floor around her. *Life* showed a photo of a propeller, or thruster, in her bow. Yes, her bow. This is a propeller that can swivel in a circle to maneuver *Deep Diver*. *Life* called the craft a "shuttle bus" to the bottom of the sea.

Popular Science had an article by Ed Link about *Deep Diver* in July, 1967. "Here," wrote Ed Link, "is a breakthrough in the conquest of the deep—a 'taxi' for undersea construction and repair workers. And there are glamorous and dramatic uses —treasure hunting, lifesaving—for such a craft." Link went on:

This contrasts with conducting sea-bottom operations remotely, all the way from the surface, with divers "hanging on a string." It eliminates need of a surface diving tender, with four-point mooring—which may have to be repositioned, by trial and error, until it is over the right spot. *Deep Diver* seeks out the objective and puts divers right there.

You enter *Deep Diver* through a hatch atop a conning tower that is ringed with eight ports. These give the pilot a full-circle view. Thirteen more windows, in the two compartments, aid in reconnoitering a work site and planning the divers' work before they go outside. . . .

. . . *Deep Diver* can maneuver in tighter places than a submarine has ever been in before. Not only does it go forward or backward. It has complete three-axis control at zero speed, unique for submarines; it can move up, down, or sideways, turn clear around, or be put in any attitude, while it is motionless in other respects.

Deep Diver is a little yellow submarine: 27 feet long, 5 feet in beam, only 8¼ tons in weight. She was kept small because Ed Link insisted she had to be light enough in weight to be lifted easily by a ship's small hydraulic crane, into and out of the sea, and to be transportable by airplane. She carries four men, can dive 1,350 feet. "We feel," Chet Smith told me, "that once we can get out and work at 1,000 feet this will cover 95 percent of the bottom-of-the-sea exploration for the next ten or fifteen years." In other words, *Deep Diver* can explore the continental shelf. Beyond 1,000 feet, Smith said, is where mechanical arms will take over from men.

Deep Diver successfully underwent tank tests on land simulating pressures up to 1,505 feet. She will not collapse till she reaches a depth of 3,300 feet.

Driven by electric storage batteries beneath the sea, as is every undersea vehicle except nuclear-powered submarines, *Deep Diver* can cruise at 3 knots for 30 minutes or at 2 knots for 6 hours. On the surface she can cruise at 3.75 knots for 30 minutes (toward her mother ship to be picked up, for example), or at half a knot for 18 hours. She moves upward or downward at exactly the same speed; *Deep Diver* climbs or descends at a rate of 2 feet a second.

What makes it possible for *Deep Diver* to place divers outside on the bottom of the sea is her lock-out chamber—a compartment that, like a diving bell, and like Lindbergh and Stenuit's SPID, can be pressurized to match the surrounding water pressure before the exit hatch is opened. After the divers return to the submarine and seal the hatch, the lock-out compartment serves as a decompression chamber in which the pressure is gradually reduced to normal surface pressure. The divers thus can be decompressed at the very same time they are being returned to the surface.

Lockheed's *Deep Quest* is the second submarine to have a lock-out chamber and so be able to place divers on the bottom. Another will be the Grumman *GSV-1*. So successful has *Deep Diver* been in her first journeys to the bottom of the sea that three more like her are being built or are planned—another for Ed Link and two for T. A. Pryor, an ocean explorer in Hawaii.

Deep Diver should help the offshore petroleum industry. She can reach bottom-of-the-sea wells present—and future. Most offshore oil wells are under 240 feet or less of sea. One has been drilled 632 feet down by Standard Oil (Esso), off California, and one has been drilled 600 feet deep off Vancouver Island, Canada. Most oil is believed to be farther out, under deeper water, and there has not been a submarine that could operate as a shuttle bus to take men down to, and bring them up from, deeper sea bottoms. *Deep Diver* can. Ocean Systems has been helping Esso Norway, Incorporated, an affiliate of the Standard Oil Company of New Jersey, drill an oil well at 450 feet down in the North Sea. Esso expects to drill often beneath 600 feet of sea. "The oil industry," Chet Smith said, "needs us badly. They're moving out into deeper water." He thinks mining the sea floor, at least under shallow water, is another activity in *Deep Diver's* future. "So far," he told me, "undersea mining is still a low-volume thing—that is, diamonds off Africa. But someone will get nodules off the ocean floor fairly soon." Most nodule (manganese, cobalt, copper, nickel, iron) deposits so far located (by trawl or deep-sea photos from the surface) are in mid-ocean water three miles deep or deeper, or on the Blake Plateau half a mile down off the Southeast Coast of the United States, too deep for *Deep Diver*. But that there are raw materials within her reach is sure from surveys made of the continental shelf by the U.S. Coast and Geodetic Survey and others. And *Deep Diver* is the first vessel that can let men step out and collect or help mine those minerals. She is the world's first diver submarine.

The Mile-Deep Journey

11

It was gray . . . dim . . . rocky . . . shadowy. That was how the bottom of the sea looked, 6,000 feet down. That was how it looked to the two men, William Ogg Rainnie, Jr., and Marvin J. McCamis, in the first submarine, the *Alvin*, ever to reach over a mile down.

The occasion, on July 20, 1965, was a turning-point in deep-sea exploration. It was the day when man, having reached the depths of the ocean, began firsthand the exploration of the bottom of the sea in his new deep-diving submarines. It was one of man's first looks at a dark world he had previously seen only a few times from bathyscaphes, and knew mainly from what his underwater cameras had shown him and from the rocks and sands and fish and animals he had hauled up from the bottom.

In April, 1963, the U.S.S. *Thresher*, a nuclear attack submarine, had sunk in 8,400 feet of water east of Cape Cod. There were no deep-diving submarines in the United States or in the world that could dive to where it was thought her wreckage lay. The United States used the bathyscaphe *Trieste* —the only vehicle of any kind we had that could go deep enough to take men down to the debris of *Thresher*. It was over two years later when the *Alvin*, built by Litton Industries, owned by the Office of Naval Research, and operated by Woods Hole, made her first 6,000-foot dive. Deep-diving submarines are ships of the late 1960's. That is how brand-new they are.

In 1962, three years before the *Alvin's* record dive, John Glenn had orbited the earth three times in his one-man Mercury spaceship. So had Malcolm Scott Carpenter (an astronaut who since has turned to exploring the sea). In 1961, Russia's Yuri A. Gagarin had made one orbit. In 1961, Russia's Gherman S. Titov had made a 17-orbit journey in space. In June, 1965—a month before the *Alvin's* dive—James A. McDivitt and Edward H. White had made a 62-orbit voyage in a two-man Gemini spacecraft. During the flight, White left the capsule and made a walk in space that lasted from over Hawaii to over the East Coast of the United States. Russia's Alexei A. Leonov had walked in space in March, 1965. Accordingly, both Russia and the United States were far along in space when the *Alvin* went down to the over-a-mile-deep bottom of the sea. That, too, shows how new deep-diving submarines are.

The *Alvin's* journey to the bottom of the sea had been a dream in the mind of an ocean scientist. He was Allyn Vine. Vine, an oceanographer at Woods Hole, believed that deep-diving submarines would help the explorers of the ocean, and had advocated that the *Alvin* be built. She is named after him.

The *Alvin* was first sent down unmanned—to 7,500 feet at the end of 10,000 feet of braided nonspin polypropylene line. A 1,200-pound anchor attached to her bottom hauled her down. She returned an echo on a surface echo-sounder all the way down to 7,000 feet. She was brought up with no leakage. She could, therefore, carry men into great depths.

The *Alvin* made her first dive to the deep sea floor in the Tongue of the Ocean. The Tongue is on the doorstep of Andros Island, the biggest island in the Bahamas.

"The Tongue of the Ocean," Don Deaton, the News Bureau editor of the Bahamas Ministry of Tourism, tells me, "is a mysterious depression in the Atlantic more than a mile deep." It is hemmed in by shallow water, islands, and shoals. It is usually free of clouds, fog, and stormy weather. A gigantic reef in the Tongue, off Andros Island's east coast, is the second biggest reef on earth—after the Great Barrier Reef, Australia. The Tongue of the Ocean is in the midst of 70,000 square miles of some of the best sport fishing in the world. Many of the world's record biggest fish have been taken in the Bahamas. Game fish abound: tuna, amberjack, bluefin tuna (giants—the Bahamas record is 814 pounds), blue marlin (the record, made in 1962, was 755 pounds), dolphin, grouper, sailfish.

Despite all those game fish on or near the surface, Deaton says, the Tongue is "almost devoid of animal noises." It is the home of the United States Navy's Atlantic Undersea Test and Evaluation Center, or AUTEC—the scientific brains of naval defense, Deaton calls it. AUTEC tests antisubmarine weapons, sonar, acoustical detection, and weapons propulsion. The Tongue is a bit of the sea where Russian trawlers appear more and more frequently. I have heard that Russian submarines sit beneath its surface and try to listen in on what we are doing.

AUTEC, set up by a United States-British-Bahamas agreement, is working on a system to "fingerprint," by the sound she makes, any submarine or any other ship in the world—American, neutral, allied, or enemy. It is planned that once this system is perfected, sonar will listen to a ship and identify her at once by her distinctive engine noises, as well as by her other sounds. Commander Mike Miller of AUTEC points out one reason the *Alvin* made her record dive in the Tongue of the Ocean: Here it takes a surface ship only 15 minutes to travel from her dock to water 6,000 feet deep. The *Alvin's* surface ship, towed by Ed Link's *Sea Diver*, transported her to the Tongue from a hangar at Cape Kennedy, Florida, where she had been made ready at the space center.

The *Alvin* started down into the 6,000 feet at 10:54 A.M. on July 20, 1965.

So new was the *Alvin* at the time that there were only three men in the world who had been trained to pilot her:

Rainnie, McCamis, and Valentine Wilson. All three work for Woods Hole. Wilson stayed above, on the surface ship, to help on this first deep dive.

Rainnie and McCamis were in their seats inside the *Alvin's* pressure hull, a 7-foot-in-diameter steel ball that resists the pressure of the depths. They could not leave the pressure hull to walk around because all other parts of the *Alvin* are open to the sea. As in most deep-diving submarines, they—like astronauts in space capsules—had to sit in one place for their entire round trip.

The *Alvin* could not have been built before the 1960's. Her pressure hull is of a new high-strength steel, 1.33 inches thick. It has been developed from the steel used in nuclear submarines. The *Alvin* is short, only 22 feet long; 8 feet in beam; and she displaces 13 tons. She is battery powered, has a big propeller at her stern that drives and turns like a rudder to steer her, and has two small propellers that point upward to let her hover and to help her move up or down in the water.

On the descent, Pilot Rainnie stopped the *Alvin* every 1,000 feet to check her instruments and determine how she was functioning.

At 4,500 feet, the big main propeller at the stern stopped working.

The *Alvin* kept going down, using her small lift propellers to push her downward.

The *Alvin* reached the bottom of the sea at 6,000 feet and parked there, at 1:37 P.M. The *Alvin* had made the first thousand-fathom dive by a submarine in history.

Rainnie and Copilot McCamis could see nothing till they switched on their floodlights. Then they observed that gray, blurry, indistinct world, and they saw rock outcroppings.

They saw a benthosaurus—a mysterious fish that sits on three long legs and had been seen only once before, from a bathyscaphe.

They saw other fish. They saw mounds made by bottom dwellers. They took movies.

After 20 minutes on the bottom the lift propellers, which

were being used to steer the *Alvin*, conked out. The *Alvin* now was at the bottom on what was at that time the deepest dive in history by a submarine—with all three of her propellers dead. None worked till the main prop again operated when the *Alvin* was back on the surface.

Rainnie and McCamis stayed 27 minutes on the bottom. Then, using the variable ballast system, they ascended. They arrived at the surface in what was for the Tongue of the Ocean a rough sea. They were picked up by their tender. This journey to the bottom of the sea that opened a new era was described laconically—and in spite of the failure of the propellers:

"Uneventful."

The problems encountered with the propellers were located and corrected before further deep dives were attempted.

The *Alvin* since has returned to or near a depth of 6,000 feet a number of times. (Two submarines, *Aluminaut* and *Deep Quest*, have gone deeper.)

Off St. David's Island, Bermuda, the *Alvin* reached 6,000 feet for the second time. Off Argus Island, near Bermuda, she made two other 6,000-foot dives. On other trips into the depths, she reached 5,850 feet in the Tongue of the Ocean and 5,900 feet off Argus Island. The 5,850-foot dive was the first made with one pilot, McCamis, and one scientific observer, Dr. Robert Hassler of Woods Hole. The *Alvin*'s mechanical arm, with two plankton sampling nets, took samples near the bottom—a task very difficult with a surface towed net.

Later, the *Alvin* went 4,900 feet down in Oceanographer's Canyon in the bottom of the sea off Woods Hole, Massachusetts.

"It was," Jim Trumbull of the United States Geological Survey, who was along, told me later, "our first look at the bedrock that underlies the continental shelf."

The *Alvin* poked up and down over 2,900 feet of the canyon's walls—from a depth of 4,973 feet to a depth of 2,073 feet. The men aboard examined the walls inch-by-inch and took rock samples.

"The cliff," said Trumbull, "was vertical as the side of a skyscraper. It took a high degree of maneuverability to examine the cliff. *Alvin* could do it. With her nose to the cliff, she moved a few feet whenever the pilot pushed a lever."

At the very bottom of the canyon, the *Alvin's* men found the sediment on the canyon floor moving seaward. It carried with it large blocks of rock. The currents in the canyon, and the origin of the canyon itself, are still being studied. "The origins of canyons," said Trumbull, "are one of the biggest unsolved mysteries we have on the bottom of the ocean."

In rough weather off Woods Hole—waves 8 feet high—when the *Alvin* was trying to enter the lifting cradle of her mother ship, *Lulu*, a wave smashed the *Alvin* against the vessel. The *Alvin's* mechanical arm was broken off and sank. So did a tray in which the *Alvin* brings up samples from the bottom. Incredibly, three weeks later, in 4,300 feet of water, the *Alvin's* crew found and recovered the arm and the tray. It took her three dives, and she had to search two square miles of the bottom of the sea.

On Dive 202, July 6, 1967, the *Alvin* became the first deep-diving submarine to be attacked by a large sea animal. She was 1,985 feet down and on the bottom of the Blake Plateau. Her men were taking geophysical and geological measurements. They saw what they thought was a six-foot black rock 40 feet beyond the starboard window. The rock started moving.

Then, said E. F. K. Zarudski of Woods Hole, the observer along, "I suddenly heard a scraping sound on the hull coming forward and slightly below me. Thinking that the noise had been caused by the submarine drifting and scraping over the sea floor, I looked down and saw that we were still stationary on the bottom.

"Simultaneously with the noise, Mr. Wilson, the copilot, whose station was at the starboard window, recoiled from it exclaiming: 'We've been hit by a fish.' Indeed, outside his window we saw a large fish, apparently captive, violently trying to disengage itself and in the process tearing some of the skin and flesh off its back. A small amount of blood was flowing out of these tears."

It was a swordfish. It had been lying on the bottom about 30 feet from where the *Alvin* had landed.

It had driven its 1½-foot sword to the hilt into a joint of the *Alvin's* hull. It was now firmly wedged.

As the sword might damage the electrical wiring, the dive was cut short and the *Alvin* surfaced. The swordfish struggled periodically, but never broke free. At the surface, the fish vomited what looked like many squid.

As the *Alvin* was hoisted aboard *Lulu*, the fish struggled violently for the last time, breaking off its sword, which was left stuck in the gap on the *Alvin*. The men on *Lulu* at the time had the fish by the tail and so could hoist it aboard.

It took the crew two hours' work to remove the sword wedged in the submarine. The *Alvin* was undamaged. But had the swordfish struck one inch to the left, electrical cables might have been harmed.

The fish, *Naval Research Reviews* said, "greatly enhanced the dinner table."

New to science were three facts: that the broadbill swordfish ranges to 2,000 feet down; that it lies on the bottom; and that it can tolerate water as cold (8 degrees centigrade) as that on the Blake Plateau.

Almost 100 years ago, Jules Verne was ahead of his time. In *20,000 Leagues Under the Sea*, his *Nautilus* could dive deep, and she made many journeys to the bottom of the sea—in fiction, that is, not fact.

"Who knows," asked Jules Verne, "if in another hundred years, we may not see a second *Nautilus*?

"Progress is slow," he added.

Progress in the case of deep-diving submarines has been slow. After Jules Verne, there were no such ships for over 90 years. But at last men are exploring the depths and bottom of the sea, in the *Alvin* and *Aluminaut* and other deep-diving craft, undersea vessels that perform like Jules Verne's *Nautilus*.

The Travelers Beneath the Gulf Stream

12

The longest journey of any research submarine yet—that's what Jacques Piccard plans for the *PX-15*, the new submersible owned by the Grumman Aircraft Engineering Corporation and built under Piccard's supervision. Piccard expects a four- to six-week voyage.

The record for time spent on a long dive by a research submarine is 33 hours, and is held by *Aluminaut*. That record can be broken any day: *Aluminaut* herself can stay down 100 hours.

Piccard plans to have five men riding with him—three scientists and two technicians. They should see a great deal on their trip. *PX-15* (named the *Ben Franklin* in August, 1968) has 29 Plexiglas viewports to look out of into the depths of the sea. She has 20 searchlights to illuminate the depths.

The six men inside *PX-15* should see a good deal also because she will not make a racket and thus drive away fish and other ocean animals. She will not often use her propellers. She will drift along silently in the lower reaches of the Gulf Stream, 300 to 2,000 feet or more down. She will drift at several knots and therefore will take up to six weeks to travel from Miami,

Florida, to a point off Halifax, Nova Scotia. *Run Silent, Run Deep* was the title of a book about World War II submarines by Captain Edward L. Beach, United States Navy. Jacques Piccard is trying to give a new meaning to running silent, running deep.

Not long ago, at the Seamen's Church Institute in New York City, I listened to Piccard as he talked about his hopes and plans for the longest undersea trip by a research submarine.

"I believe," Piccard said, "that of all studies in the sea, the studies of the surface and underwater currents are the most interesting. Ponce de Leon and other sailors of the sixteenth century could save as much as one week on trips to Europe by keeping their ships in the Gulf Stream." One of Ponce de Leon's pilots, Antonio de Alaminos, is credited with being the first sailor to find the Gulf Stream, accidentally. In the year 1513, off what is now Cape Canaveral, near the location of today's space-launching pads at Cape Kennedy, Florida, one of Ponce de Leon's small sailing ships tried to anchor. But the Gulf Stream swept her out of sight, to the north, within an hour. Alaminos and the crew on another vessel watched astonished as the small ship disappeared.

The currents are one of the most important and most characteristic features of the ocean: They constantly stir up and mix the water, so that the general composition of the ocean water, with its dissolved salts, is similar everywhere. The currents carry fishes and animal life from one part of the sea to another. The Gulf Stream, for instance, moves tropical fish and turtles all the way to Woods Hole, at Cape Cod.

The Gulf Stream, which passes Miami like a millrace (at up to 5 knots) and slows down to a slow walk (1½ to 2 knots) as it crosses the Atlantic to Europe, needs to be studied. Though it is at the United States' front door—only half a mile off the Palm Beach, Florida, shore—there are still mysteries surrounding it.

Exactly what is the Gulf Stream's route up the East Coast and across the Atlantic? We don't know; we do know it moves around. Oil tankers have shown how much it twists and turns and throws off eddies. It also adds water to itself between Florida and Cape Hatteras. How? By Hatteras, it is carrying 150 million tons of water a second, five times what it had in the Straits of Florida. Does the Gulf Stream have a pulse? Some scientists think water throbs in it, like blood in a human artery. What about the counter-current beneath the Gulf Stream? Henry Strommel of Woods Hole, using Swallow floats—floats that remain at set depths beneath the surface—discovered there was beneath the Gulf Stream a massive deep current flowing in the opposite direction. "This phenomenon, when understood," says the National Geographic Society, "could revolutionize present concepts of ocean circulation systems."

Benjamin Franklin in the late 1700's recommended to American and British sailing-ship captains that they use the Gulf Stream to speed their passage from Rhode Island and other states to Europe. His great-grandson, Alexander Dallas Bache, a West Point graduate, studied the Gulf Stream as he collected weather observations. Matthew Fontaine Maury, the naval lieutenant from Virginia, in 1855, published the first text-book of modern oceanography, *Physical Geography of the Sea*, and began it with a description of the Gulf Stream: "There is a river in the ocean. In the severest droughts it never fails and in the mightiest floods it never overflows. . . . The Gulf of Mexico is its fountain, and its mouth is the Arctic Ocean."

Captain Nemo, in *20,000 Leagues*, said the ocean "has a pulse, arteries, spasms; and I agree with the learned Maury, who discovered in it a circulation as real as the circulation of blood in animals."

"Benjamin Franklin," Piccard pointed out, "made temperature measurements of the Gulf Stream to three hundred feet down. Practically all measurements today are made from the surface." He intends to remedy that, from the depths: "When underwater, we have a much better impression than on the surface."

A short dive, Piccard feels, would be inadequate to study the Gulf Stream: "With bathyscaphes you can dive for only a few hours or one day. If we want a better idea of a complex and big phenomenon like the Gulf Stream, we cannot stay only a few hours."

The very first men of all to explore the depths, and thereby prepare the way for Jacques Piccard and today's research submarines, were two Americans, William Beebe, of New York City's Bronx Zoo, and Otis Barton. In 1934, when 525 feet was the deepest a human had dived, Beebe and Barton wriggled into a steel ball called a bathysphere and had it lowered into the sea off Bermuda. If the cable to the bathysphere had snapped, the men would have been lost—they would have plummeted to the sea bottom. Through a six-inch quartz porthole they were the first men, ever, to eyewitness the weird deep-sea fish, the luminescence of the depths, and the shadowy forms of unknown creatures. At their deepest point—a half-mile down—a Flammenwerfer shrimp shot forth a cloud of luminous fluid just outside their porthole.

In the 1950's, Auguste Piccard, Jacques' father, hung a steel ball like the bathysphere beneath a long oblong float partly filled with lighter-than-water aviation gasoline. The result was the bathyscaphe. Pulled down to the bottom of the sea by weights (tons of shotgun pellets), bathyscaphes set new depth records. At the bottom they would shed some of their weights and so rise to the surface.

In a bathyscaphe, Pierre-Henri Willm and Commander Georges Houot, of the French Navy, were the first men to go over a mile down. They made it on August 14, 1953. Six weeks later, Auguste and Jacques Piccard reached a depth of almost two miles in the Tyrrhenian Sea. They saw only ghostly flickers of phosphorescence. In the bathyscaphe *Trieste* in 1959, Jacques Piccard and Dr. Andreas Rechnitzer dived to 18,050 feet and later to 23,000 feet.

Then, in 1960, Jacques Piccard and the *Trieste*, by then owned by the United States Navy, made the deepest dive of all: In the Marianas Trench of the Challenger Deep, off Guam, Piccard and Navy Lieutenant (today Lieutenant Commander) Don Walsh reached a depth of 35,800 feet, almost seven miles.

At first they got to the point where, they thought, the bottom should have been. "There is no bottom yet," Walsh said. "Maybe we missed it," answered Piccard.

At the very bottom they saw a flatfish and a red shrimp—the first eyewitness proof man had that there is life, and fish life at that, on the very bottom of the deepest sea.

At that point, said Piccard, "Walsh and I shook hands."

Their dive is still man's deepest, and will remain so unless a deeper chasm in the bottom of the sea is found—possible, but unlikely. The *Trieste* had taken them 60 times as deep as World War II submarines could safely go. Then the *Trieste* came straight up. Bathyscaphes, the deepest-diving vehicles of all, are like elevators. They go straight down and up. They do not have a capacity to cruise over the bottom of the sea as do today's research submarines.

Having made the longest (in terms of depth) trip man ever made under the sea, Jacques Piccard now wants to make the longest in terms of time and mileage.

What will his men do? Why is it important to dive in the Gulf Stream? Grumman Aircraft asked several hundred scientists to suggest problems. But, Piccard says, there are two main groups of questions:

(1) "Acoustical problems. There are lots of noises in the sea. Often we don't hear them. There is the noise of water moving sand on the bottom. There are underwater volcanoes or earthquakes. There is the noise of the waves. There is the noise produced by sea animals. Shrimps, fishes, whales, and porpoises make noises. Besides, there are noises made by surface boats or by submarines." Anything men can learn about underwater sound will be useful in national defense, in operating and further developing sonar, and in developing communications beneath the sea. "Because we don't make any noise our-

selves," Piccard said, "but will be completely silent, we will have a good opportunity to listen to the sound at the depths."

(2) "Another big field is marine biology and zoology observations. We will be in a good position to see fishes. Floating and drifting with the current, we will have no speed in relation to the water or the fish. When we descend in a bathyscaphe, it makes turbulence and fishes disappear. In the *PX-15*, we expect to be surrounded by thousands of fishes. We may have to use the propeller to make turbulence to get rid of them."

The trip of *PX-15* will be man's first chance, from beneath the sea, to watch marine life in its environment for an extended time.

Piccard is probably right that a submarine running silently and running deep may attract sea life around it. Jules Verne thought it would.

In *20,000 Leagues*, Verne imagined that fish would accompany submarines. "For two whole hours," he wrote, "an aquatic army escorted the *Nautilus*. During their games, their bounds, while rivalling each other in beauty, brightness, and velocity, I distinguished the green labre; the banded mullet, marked by a double line of black; the round-tailed goby. . . ."

What limited experience men have had in such a situation has shown that this is likely to occur. On November 7, 1964, off California in the Westinghouse-Jacques-Yves Cousteau diving saucer, Pilot Raymond ("Canoe") Kientzy and Scripps Institution's professor of submarine geology, Dr. Francis Parker Shepard, had their visibility cut at a depth of between 300 and 400 feet. The reason: fish—and more fish—especially young ones. "In fact," reported Dr. Shepard, "it was one thing that made visibility poor—there were just clouds of small fish."

At the Bureau of Commercial Fisheries Biological Laboratory in Honolulu, Reginald M. Gooding built a raft with an undersea view from a many-windowed caisson beneath the waterline. In 1964, as the raft floated silently on the Pacific surface, one man at a time descended into the caisson and looked out into the sea. Observers included Gooding, John J. Magnuson, and Randolph K. C. Chang. Reports the Bureau:

"When the raft was first put into the water, no fish were to be seen. Within ten minutes the first of them arrived, little rudderfish that are cousins of the Hawaiian nenue, for which the raft is named. Dolphinfish, known as mahimahi in Hawaii, appeared. They mingled with triggerfish, close relatives of the Hawaiian humuhumunukunukuapuaa, and many others. Within a short time, numerous fishes had been sighted. By the end of the longer drifts, almost a thousand fishes and other creatures were swimming within sight. . . . The length of these creatures ranged from a few inches to several feet. The observations on these drifts constitute the most exhaustive study yet made on an underwater community in the open sea."

The nuclear submarine *Skate*, heading for the North Pole, ran into a tremendous school of fishes, her captain, Commander (now Rear Admiral) James Calvert, United States Navy, reported. He saw the school on closed-circuit TV from a TV camera mounted outside the hull: "Suddenly the screen was flooded with fish. . . . Individually they were very small—no more than eight inches long—but their numbers seemed countless. Men came from all over the ship to watch the show. Here we were, four hundred feet below the surface and less than three hundred miles from the North Pole—what sort of fish could they be? No one could be sure, but both Dr. Waldo Lyon and Walt Wittman thought they most closely resembled ordinary North Atlantic herring. The school was enormous. On we went, mile after mile, and the sea appeared full of fish." A big shadowy shape appeared, perhaps a shark or seal. Eventually, the submarine cruised out of the fish school. "Who knows," asked Calvert, "how many other displays of nature we missed beneath the Arctic ice simply for lack of eyes to see them?"

In the North Atlantic, Captain Bill Gray of the Miami Seaquarium points out, the rudderfish accompanies floating planks or logs and makes a home in floating boxes or barrels—and so might accompany Piccard's *PX-15*. The young rudderfish swims beneath the Portuguese man-of-war, a jellyfish with 100-foot-long stinging tentacles. Although other sea creatures are stung and eaten by the man-of-war, the rudderfish is never harmed.

Jacques Piccard and his crew will be in a position to see for themselves what goes on beneath the Gulf Stream. And, like the *Skate*, they will have TV mounted on the outer hull of *PX-15* to assist their eyesight.

PX-15 is a 48.7-foot-long steel cylinder with 1.4-inch-thick walls. She travels at five to six knots when her four 25-horsepower electric motors are driving her small propellers. She weighs 130 tons. *PX-15's* inside diameter is 10 feet. Living quarters for her men and the galley are at her stern. The central control station for her pilot is at the bow. A central corridor runs throughout her length.

After her drift beneath the Gulf Stream, *PX-15*, Grumman says, will be brought into a shipyard, taken entirely apart, and studied in every detail. Then she will be reassembled, with some changes, into a new work boat, *GSV-1*. *GSV-1*, among other things, will let divers step outside onto the ocean floor at as deep as 1,000 feet. *GSV-1* will have legs added to her so she can squat on the ocean bottom. She will have drills to sample the floor. She will have a manipulator, or mechanical arm, to lift heavy loads. One of her goals is to lead the way to recovering used missiles and rocket launchers and other heavy valuable hardware of the space age that now often is lost or used only once.

The mesoscaphe (boat for the middle depths) *PX-15* was primarily constructed by Giovanola in Monthey, Switzerland, then shipped to the Grumman base at West Palm Beach, Florida. Giovanola in 1963-4 built Jacques Piccard's and the world's first and only other mesoscaphe. This one, the *Auguste Piccard*, 98 feet long, made 1,100 dives to the bottom of Lake Geneva, Switzerland. She carried as many as 45 people a trip—30,000 passengers altogether. The passengers saw a flat, rather monotonous landscape. They looked out through 45 Plexiglas ports, and were aided by 61 powerful searchlights. Piccard's first mesoscaphe thus demonstrated one way you or I or anyone else will soon be making journeys to the bottom of the sea. She was the first submarine in history for relaxation and observation by the average man.

The man in the street and his youngsters and wife will not be able to sail beneath the Gulf Stream on the voyage of *PX-15*. But Piccard, who has a wife, Marie-Claude, two sons, and one daughter, will be showing how one day soon families may be able to take vacation cruises to see the ocean—from beneath it.

The Trip to Four Miles Down

13

"I worked topside when Don Walsh and Jacques Piccard made their almost seven-mile dive off Guam," Larry Shumaker said to me. "I was taking turns diving with Walsh. The deepest dive came on his day to go down.

"My turn came a day or so later. I made a dive of twenty thousand feet deep in *Trieste*. It was the first time I'd gone that deep."

That makes Larry Shumaker, 35 years old, one of the few men ever to have been to a depth of 20,000 feet—a depth new Navy rescue, search, and recovery submarines are planned eventually to reach. So far no submarines can go that deep; only bathyscaphes can, and they have not made many journeys to the bottom of the sea that far down.

Shumaker was born at Southgate, California, near Los Angeles. He graduated from the Naval Academy in 1954. Don Walsh was his classmate there. Shumaker served first aboard destroyers. In 1957 he went to submarine school. "Then I was on submarines," he says. "*K-3*, *Rasher*, and *Bonita;* I was exec (executive officer) on *Caiman* and *Capitaine*."

In 1958, the United States Navy bought the *Trieste* from

her inventor, Auguste Piccard, and made her the first research submersible in the United States. The Navy Electronics Laboratory, San Diego, operated her till 1964. (The *Trieste* has been succeeded by *Trieste II*.)

Trieste became flagship to the Electronics Lab—the only noncommissioned vessel, I believe, ever to serve as a flagship.

Shumaker became a *Trieste* pilot in 1958. That gives him almost ten years' experience in the deep sea today. He is the only man alive, with the exception of Jacques-Yves Cousteau, Jacques Piccard, and Andreas Rechnitzer, who has had such a long time at deep-diving. "I've got the longest time in the U.S.," he grins. That is how new deep-diving is: The American veteran is 35, with ten years' experience.

On his 20,000-foot dive off Guam, Shumaker ran out of sunlight after a few hundred feet. "Down below where the sunlight penetrates," he told me, "the ocean becomes a pretty fascinating place."

Luminescent animals swam all around him. "We saw a few sardine-type fish—and deeper types with long tails."

The bottom, almost four miles down, he says, was "most interesting. There were rock formations two to three feet high. There was a lot of fine, silky sand. There were little worm tubes indicating life.

"My granddad was the curator of a marine museum in Los Angeles. To see these things where they live for the first time is a gripping experience."

I asked Shumaker if he thought the Navy would succeed in developing submarines that would dive 20,000 feet. "Yes," he said, "they'll get there."

His *Trieste* dive convinced him that 20,000-foot-deep submarine journeys are practical.

Shumaker once made a dive in Cousteau's diving saucer, *Soucoupe*. "It was off La Jolla, California, in five hundred fifty feet of water, in Scripps Canyon," he says. He saw ledges overhanging the canyon. Previously, he and Bob Dill had seen Scripps Canyon in *Trieste*. "In the *Soucoupe*," he said, "we could get to shallower, steeper positions.

"The canyon area is full of animal life. So is the deeper sea round it. Starfish are abundant in the ocean off California—there are many brittle stars with their long arms. There is a sea cucumber with legs that walks around the bottom. There are small red rockfish. But the most common of all animal life off Southern California is the black sea cod, three or four feet long, two or three thousand feet down."

Shumaker has a new job: He is chief pilot for Lockheed's *Deep Quest.*

Shumaker is married to the former Ione Beck, a Michigan girl. They have four children: Lawrence, 10; Kurt, 8; Erica, 6; Suzanne, 2. He likes to tell tales of his adventures to his youngsters: for example, about the time he saw a deep-water shark when he was diving in the *Trieste* in the Atlantic while searching for the *Thresher.* "There was a long-tailed shark around there," he says, "with a long, ribbon-like tail streaming out behind and rippling as it swam along."

On the bottom of the sea, 20,000 feet beneath the surface, Larry Shumaker in 1960 demonstrated one thing: the exploration of the deep ocean at last was practicable. At 35,800 feet down, Jacques Piccard and Don Walsh had demonstrated the same fact. On the bottom of the sea at different depths, so had Auguste Piccard, Willm, Houot, Rechnitzer, Tailliez, Cousteau, and other pilots and scientists aboard bathyscaphes. With bathyscaphes, mankind's exploration of the depths and bottom of the sea at last could begin. The men in bathyscaphes led the way for the men in today's deep-diving submarines.

Larry Shumaker feels fortunate to have been in bathyscaphes, to be today in deep-diving submarines, and at 35 years old to be a veteran traveler to the bottom of the sea. "I've got some of the explorer in me," he says. "We all have. I wanted to do something new and different. I was lucky enough to get to do it."

Men and Metal
Under Pressure

14

A deep-diving research submarine was planned and built to operate at a depth of 6,000 feet. She was tested on dry land to see if she measured up to her builder's hopes.

She did.

She did better.

The test showed she could operate safely at a depth of 8,500 feet. Her maximum operational depth was accordingly increased from 6,000 to 8,000 feet (over a mile and a half).

The submarine was Lockheed's *Deep Quest*, today piloted by Larry Shumaker.

She is a stubby, flattened-out shark-shaped submarine. Her insides consist largely of two 7-foot-in-diameter spheres, or balls, of high-strength steel, lined up in a straight line. These spheres intersect—they are connected to each other by a watertight door through which men may pass from one to the other. The stern sphere is a pressure chamber in which divers can be made ready to leave *Deep Quest* at depths up to 1,000 feet. The other holds the crew and any scientists or passengers.

The men are protected inside the spheres by the high-strength steel that forms them and makes up the pressure hull. It is a new kind of metal, called maraging steel.

The outer hull—the stubby shark-shaped hull that gives *Deep Quest* her outer appearance—is of aluminum.

Deep Quest is 16 feet in hull beam, 19 feet at her maximum width, and 39 feet 10 inches long. She displaces 50 tons, or about the weight of an average sperm whale. Her battery power permits her to remain submerged for 24 hours. She has full life support for four men aboard for 48 hours.

Two 7½-horsepower alternating-current motors in her stern drive her at a maximum speed of 5 knots.

She is able to carry 7,000 pounds (a very heavy load) to that 8,000-foot depth. Some of her cargoes will be specialized scientific instruments. Her crew of two can take along two scientists or observers to run the instruments.

Deep-diving submarines these days are tested on dry land before they ever go on journeys to the bottom of the sea. Not all pass their test. At least one cracked up in a dry-land test as this book was written.

The pressure hull of *Deep Quest* was taken from the Lockheed company at Sunnyvale, California, to the Southwest Research Institute on the outskirts of landlocked San Antonio, Texas. SwRI, as it is known, has tested many research submarines, among them *Aluminaut*, the *Alvin*, the *Deep Jeep*, and *Deepstar 4000*. All these passed their test and went on to the depths of the sea.

At SwRI, *Deep Quest's* pressure hull was lowered into a deep-ocean simulator, a large, upright cylinder 90 inches in diameter with steel walls 4½ inches thick. It is inside a silo.

Its size—it is the largest such pressure chamber in existence —actually dictated to Lockheed the size of *Deep Quest's* pressure hull. The deep-ocean simulator was built to test submersibles, and for the simulator as well as for *Deep Quest*, the test, in May, 1966, was the first run.

The *Deep Quest* pressure hull was lowered by crane into the simulator, with inches to spare. A 15-ton, 13-inch closure plate on top of the simulator was shut tightly.

The pressure hull previously had been subjected to tests simulating 14 lesser dives. Now it was the big one—a deep dive which would, if successful, show that the hull could withstand a pressure of 3,750 pounds per square inch.

Dr. Robert C. DeHart, director of structural research at SwRI, announced the test would begin.

Three thousand gallons of oil were pumped into the simulator. The pressure inside on *Deep Quest's* pressure hull gradually was built up.

A deeply-concerned knot of men watched the test from a reinforced concrete bunker—a precaution against debris from a possible blowout.

Scientists and engineers studied instruments to see what was happening. The readouts were coming from 440 strain gauges and from displacement measuring devices. R. N. Dippy and J. H. Diffenderfer, engineers from Sunship Company, Chester, Pennsylvania, which had built the pressure hull for Lockheed, watched the strain-gauge readings that showed how the hull was performing.

Pete Summers, *Deep Quest* program manager at Lockheed, joined SwRI research engineer Edward Briggs. The men huddled over a chart. It showed that, as the pressure increased, the stresses increased according to predictions.

The tension among the men increased, too.

The needle in a pressure gauge edged its way up. It moved toward the pressure the hull would encounter at 8,500 feet— 500 feet beyond the planned test depth.

Horacio Basserga, a Lockheed engineer, took out his slide rule and made a few calculations.

Four SwRI technicians called out the strain gauge readings, which were entered at once into the test log.

"Eight thousand feet and the hull is behaving perfectly."

The pointer inched its way toward the goal: the pressure at 8,500 feet down in the sea.

"Admiral Pete Summers," SwRI reports, "looked to engineer Basserga. They nodded to each other reassuringly. SwRI president Martin Goland nodded a go-ahead.

"Take her down to eighty-five hundred."

It was all systems go—or bust.

"The pump wheezed away," says SwRI, "forcing the hydraulic pressure up until finally the submarine was resting at the equivalent pressure encountered at 8,500 feet . . . 3,750 pounds on each square inch of surface. [At sea level, normal atmospheric pressure is 15 pounds per square inch.] The hull had performed even better than expected at depths beyond the most optimistic operating limits.

"The Texas sun had almost disappeared behind the hill. 'Let's take the pressure down,' said Basserga. 'We'll take the hull out in the morning.'

"The next morning, the crane slowly lifted the 15-ton lid off its new SwRI pressure vessel and beyond the myriad wires which reached toward the gauges you could see the outline of the white hull.

"As the pumping out operation for the test chamber proceeded, the hatch appeared and then half of the top sphere. Now less than half an inch of freeboard was present between the craft and the edge of the test vessel."

At this point, a bosun's chair was attached to a portable crane over the submarine's pressure hull. Summers and Basserga were to be lowered into the top sphere and to its bottom. (The bottom sphere had been filled with sandbag ballast to prevent its floating and banging against the sides of the tank.)

There were no signs of any leakage whatever into the submarine. Even the viewports had passed the test.

Deep Quest was hauled up and out of the deep-ocean simulator. Even the joint where the two spheres join each other had passed the test with flying colors.

How two spheres could be joined without causing a weak spot that might give way under pressure was a difficult problem. "We have solved the problem of intersecting pressure vessels," says J. G. Wenzel, manager of Lockheed's ocean systems and deep submergence program. That problem, he explains, is that the pressure everywhere across the joint must be the same as that on the walls of the two spheres. It took a tremendous amount of analysis to figure out a solution.

Providing the men aboard *Deep Quest* with two spheres gives them more room—more space per man. *Deep Quest* has 64.1 cubic feet per man for a four-man crew and 85.4 cubic feet apiece for a three-man crew. A one-man Mercury spaceship provided 48 cubic feet for the astronaut. The two-man Gemini spaceships each had 53 cubic feet for each astronaut. The spacemen aboard the three-man Apollo, or moon, spaceships have 75 cubic feet apiece.

Inside *Deep Quest*, as inside all other submarines, men breathe air at normal atmospheric pressure. If *Deep Quest's* system to provide air to the men aboard her ever breaks down, even on the bottom of the sea, the men will have a chance to survive. They will use an emergency system that took six months to develop.

They will put on face masks and strap on regulators and breathing bags very similar to those worn by scuba divers. Long hoses will run to breathing-gas supplies in the aft sphere.

The *Deep Quest* system uses lithium hydroxide to absorb the poisonous carbon dioxide that men breathe out. Lithium hydroxide was used to absorb CO_2 in the capsules of the United States' two-man Gemini space flights.

The *Deep Quest* system was tested by four men. For three hours, using it, they made notes, did deep knee bends, and did work such as they would have to do aboard *Deep Quest* in an emergency.

Everything proved satisfactory. This means that the crew and scientists using their emergency breathing system can get back to the surface from a depth of 8,500 feet. Three hours is more than time enough.

To support *Deep Quest* at sea, Lockheed is building a unique support ship that has a well, like a Navy landing ship dock, into which *Deep Quest* will sail. An elevator in the well can be lowered, as a dry dock can be sunk when a ship is to be repaired. Then *Deep Quest* can enter and be lifted up. "This," says William B. Parhan, chief of Lockheed's ocean systems support operations, "will let us inspect and maintain the boat while we're still on location."

The Lockheed support ship is called *Sub-porter* (for submarine supporter). *Sub-porter* is 108 feet long and displaces 425 tons.

When, at the end of her dry-land pressure test at San Antonio, *Deep Quest* was hauled out of the deep-ocean simulator, something amazing came into view. Inside the simulator, she had been wedged into place by 4-by-4-inch timbers. They had been twisted and compressed by the pressure into something like crippled 2-by-2's.

In spite of the timbers' squashing, *Deep Quest* herself was unscathed. As SwRI put it, she had "maintained her integrity."

The pressure hull was inspected electronically for flaws. Sound waves were shot into her; their echoes bounced back. There were no flaws of significance.

Deep Quest next was X-rayed. In fact, she was inspected ultrasonically and radiographically four different times. She passed every inspection.

She had been planned over several years largely by computer and electronic data processing. "One of the most significant things," said Pete Summers, "is that the actual data obtained from these tests almost exactly matched our predictions every foot of the way from the surface to pressure depths of eighty-five hundred feet."

But what mattered most was that final test in the deep-ocean simulator. "When you're working with sophisticated structures and advanced materials technology like our maraging steels," Summers said, "the real proof is in testing the full-scale hardware."

Deep Quest was ready now to be covered with her aluminum outer hull. She was ready now to make journeys to the bottom of the sea.

She was painted white and orange, with her conning tower and tail bright orange. On September 30, 1967, she made her first test dive. At 9:06 A.M., seven miles south of Point Loma, near San Diego, she submerged. Aboard were Chief Pilot Larry Shumaker, Pilot Glenn F. Minard, Project Manager Pete Summers, and Electronics Technician Marshall E. Woy. Ten minutes later, Shumaker called his support ship (until *Sub-porter* is built), *Transquest*, on the surface: "*Transquest, Transquest,* this is *Deep Quest.* We're on the bottom at a hundred and thirty-five feet. It's beautiful down here, and all systems are go." Pilots Shumaker and Minard cruised *Deep Quest* more than half a mile across the sandy bottom. Then *Deep Quest* ascended. At 10:24 A.M., Pilot Minard radioed, "*Transquest, Transquest,* this is *Deep Quest,* we are on the surface. Everything is OK."

Summers said everything went fine, and *Deep Quest* made progressively deeper dives. In January, 1968, she made the world's deepest submarine dive, 6,300 feet. An 8,000-foot dive was planned for her. "When we make that eight-thousand-foot dive," Shumaker told me, "I'll carry the forty-nine-star flag I had on my twenty-thousand-foot dive in *Trieste.*" He would also, he said, take coffee in a thermos bottle and prepared food like sandwiches—*Deep Quest* has no cooking facilities. That dive—to 8,310 feet—was made February 28, 1968. Shumaker did have that flag along.

Ahead lay more journeys to the bottom of the sea for *Deep Quest.* She can dive deeper than any submarine in the seas except *Aluminaut. Deep Quest* may make tremendously exciting discoveries on the bottom of the ocean.

But whatever her crew and scientists see at the depths, they will never be thrilled more than were *Deep Quest's* builders on that day at San Antonio when she passed her final dry-land examination.

The Black
Rock

15

"I wish I could convey to you," Dick Usry told me, "the anticipation and curiosity we feel on every dive as we approach the bottom. We have been watching it come close on the Fathometer's paper trace. We release the weight and start drifting down.

"Our lights are on and we are straining our eyes against the viewport. The backscatter from the lights creates a white haze below us which we often mistake for the bottom."

Dick Usry is chief pilot of *Deepstar 4000*, the Westinghouse—Cousteau submersible that can dive 4,000 feet—four-fifths of a mile.

In May, 1966, off San Diego, California, 15 miles west of Point Loma, she dived to that capacity depth—for the first time. Behind Dick Usry, who was aboard, were many dives to depths of 1,000 feet or less off California in Captain Jacques-Yves Cousteau's diving saucer. "They provided crew training for the *DS-4000*," Usry explains. Cousteau himself helped design and build *Deepstar 4000*.

Behind Usry and his crew—Joe Thompson and Ron Church—there lay over 70 shallow *Deepstar 4000* dives that assured their training and the preparation of the submarine. "Each man," says Usry, "is a specialist in his part of the vehicle's innards and takes more than average care and puts more than average attention in her condition. The dive was the culmination of months of design, construction, tests, and many long hours of preparation that had molded the pilots and crew into a group of highly motivated men."

The dive to 4,000 feet began when a crane aboard *Deepstar 4000's* mother ship, the *Burchtide*, had picked up *Deepstar* from the deck, hoisted the submarine into the air, then swung her over the side and lowered her into a calm sea. In the water outside *Deepstar*, two divers swam about the submarine, carefully checking electrical cables, fittings, and equipment to assure the pilot that the launching had not disarranged anything checked previously.

Inside *Deepstar*, Usry and his two crewmen, having closed the 3-inch-thick hatch and sealed themselves in, went over their checklist: motors, hydraulic system, sonar, oxygen supply, carbon dioxide level, and lithium hydroxide supply; the Fathometer, with three transducers (antennae) that look up at the surface, down to the ocean floor, or forward; the citizen's band radio, etc.

"Our checklist," Usry told me, "is as complex as a 727's [the Boeing jet passenger plane]. Just before we go down we are relatively calm below the surface—and busy as hell doing the checklist." Till the check is completed, a safety line runs from *Deepstar*, 40 feet below the surface, up to *Burchtide*.

Usry made a light and phone signal to the swimmers outside. They released the safety line.

Deepstar started down to her greatest depth.

Deepstar does not use her motors for descent. She is weighted—with several weights she can drop as necessary—to sink all the way. Down she went, down at a good clip, down at about 80 feet a minute.

Deepstar at all times was tracked from a small boat near *Burchtide*. A pinger on *DS-4000* emits a beep every second. The beep is followed by a directional antenna on the small boat, training around and down to get the strongest sound.

Besides, *Deepstar's* men kept chattering. On underwater telephone, they reported conditions every 300 feet of the descent to *Burchtide*. Once on the bottom, they would phone only every half hour.

After 55 minutes, *Deepstar* dropped some weight 200 feet above the bottom, lost momentum, and settled down, under power, to make her landing.

The crew switched on her lights—lights that consume more electricity than several homes.

From inside, three faces gazed through her 4.4-inches-in-diameter and 4-inches-in-thickness Plexiglas ports. Two of the men were lying prone on couches; one, in a tilting seat near the center, had to peer over another's shoulder. "The crew," says Usry, "could not see but could distinctly sense the almost one-ton-per-square-inch pressure on the Plexiglas windows through which they peered."

He spoke into his underwater telephone. "I am at four thousand feet," he said.

His first concern on the bottom, as always, was for the safety of his vessel: "To see the bottom in time to avoid settling onto a sharp rock or dangerous object. It is also our first opportunity to verify if currents might sweep us sideways into objects out of our range of vision.

"But, aside from these technical reasons, I think we all hope to see something new or different—something really exciting and valuable never seen before. No matter how many dives you make, there is so much we still don't know down there that I guess that moment of first sighting is the most awaited time of every dive. Maybe some day we'll settle right down on a valuable mineral deposit, a lost treasure, or see a strange new animal to report to the scientists."

Usry had stopped during the feverish pre-dive preparation long enough to do something unusual: He had sewn a flag to be placed on the bottom. It was an unusual flag. Its inscription read: DS-4000/Westinghouse/1st 4,000' dive/11 May 1966.

Deep Quest *in 1968 made world's deepest dive ever by a submarine.
Lockheed craft, whose chief pilot is Larry Shumaker, is first submarine
made of high-strength maraging steel used in space-booster rockets.*

This is getting to be a standard setting for a deep dive. The catamaran (two-hulled) mother ship Transquest *is in the foreground, and* Deep Quest *is in the background.*

The beginning of the deepest trip ever made. Frogmen—standing on submerged deck—help make sure Deep Quest *is ready. Date is February 28, 1968. Place is the Pacific.*

On her way: Last frogman leaves as Deep Quest *begins trip that ended 8,310 feet below surface, 2,010 feet deeper than the previous world record depth. Crew faces peer from viewports.*

Inside Deep Quest, *Larry Shumaker, chief pilot, is at controls of the submarine. After her dive,* Deep Quest *was dismantled. Every part was X-rayed or checked.*

Alvin's *mechanical arm brings back samples of bottom.* "Alvin," *said a February 1968 Department of Defense magazine, "will open to men's eyes . . . one-sixth of the ocean floor."*

Alvin *was first deep-diving sub attacked by big fish. Swordfish lost its life. But crew wondered what if its sword had been driven straight at viewport. Tests have shown window would have withstood blow.*

Perry Cubmarine *is one of whole fleet of inexpensive submarines being built at West Palm Beach, Florida. Yacht clubs or individuals can afford to explore undersea frontiers in such craft.*

Jacques-Yves Cousteau's Diving Saucer *appeared in 1959. Her crew found a canyon with vegetation growing straight out of its steep walls: "Like looking at the tops of trees in a forest from the air."*

Pilot Bob Hill in Star II *was one of first to visit bottom of Gulf of Mexico. "Here," he said, "the Mississippi dumps its silt—an undersea dust storm. Cruising over this is like flying over a cloud."*

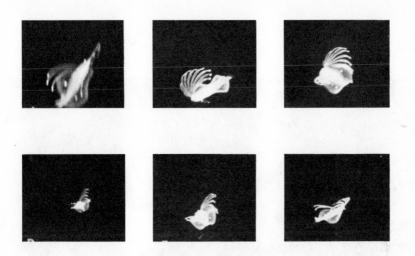

Mysterious fish was spotted from Diving Saucer *off Cabo San Lucas, Baja California. It is probably of the family Bothidae. Eric Barham and Raymond Kientzy, who saw it, call it Sally Rand, after the fan dancer.*

Star III *in Bahamas took Bob Hill 2,000 feet down to glowing shrimp and luminescent fish. "I saw them as they flashed past the viewports, the different colors going by," he said. "It was beautiful."*

The flag was held in the jaw (or hand) of *Deepstar's* mechanical arm. She planted it on the bottom mud, 4,132 feet down. "Eddy currents," Usry recalls, "from the vehicle's two propellers swirled clouds of 'dust,' bottom silt, and long-decayed organic materials about the flag.

"The crew felt as though they were making a landing on a bleak, lunar landscape. For some reason I felt almost apologetic about mankind disturbing the peace and stillness of the ocean floor."

Deepstar rested on a flat, mud floor.

Her lights pierced the awesome darkness, Usry says, for only 50 feet around the craft.

Her men drank hot chocolate from thermos jars (coffee is not wise on long dives vis-à-vis the bladder) and ate sandwiches. They cannot smoke aboard.

After taking several photographs of the flag (which would become highly prized souvenirs), the three men in the submarine looked around them and saw a welcoming committee on the sea floor.

Usry spoke into his tape recorder, on for the entire dive. "I see a brittle starfish." The brittle star, or serpent star, is the long-armed starfish whose arms are easily broken off (and almost as easily grown back). The men also saw some of the other familiar animals that are greeting men now making journeys to the bottom of the sea. The drab, gray sablefish, a North Pacific fish that's good to eat. The hagfish—the sucking, jawless, eel-like relative of the lamprey that caused devastation among Great Lakes fishes some years ago. Usry reminds me it has five hearts; he caught one later in the claw of the mechanical arm and brought it to the surface for laboratory analysis. The ratfish, *Chimaeri collei*, with its blunt snout and thread-like tail. Sea urchins, the sharp-spined, ball-shaped, crawling animal that lives on the floors of all seas everywhere and has its mouth in the middle of its bottom. "We came across a field of tulip sponges," Usry said, "three to four feet high, gently waving. We 'flew' over these like an airplane skimming treetops. Every few seconds," he recalls, "flashes from the strobe lights or the still camera captured some animal's profile or an unusual bottom feature."

Inside *Deepstar* it grew cold. The 57-degree outside water temperature was beginning to affect the steel hull. Then, in a 400-square-yard area, the three men maneuvered *Deepstar* in hovering tests, in flying-off-the-bottom tests, climbing and diving 15 to 20 feet, and in turns on her axis. Said Usry: "She handled well. All equipment operated beautifully. We were able to maneuver to photograph and to pick up samples with no difficulty." Later, he would be even better at picking up samples: With a slurp gun, or slurper—a vacuum cleaner, Usry calls it—he would capture a jellyfish-like object.

After four hours on the bottom of the sea, *Deepstar* dropped an 187-pound weight and rose to the surface—in 55 minutes, the same time she had taken to descend. "It is not particularly pleasant," Usry said later, "sitting on the surface and lolling around. On recovery, we have little to do (no checklist) until they hook on to tow us to the crane. Then we pick up the motion of the mother ship." As quickly as possible, the crane swung *Deepstar* aboard.

"In the future," Usry said, "we'll go down to a certain depth, have a quiet boat (motors off), and sit and listen to the sounds of the sea."

Deepstar 4000 is a tear-shaped submarine, 18 feet long, 7 feet high, and 11½ feet wide. She weighs nine tons. Her ball-shaped pressure hull holds the crew and protects the men against that one-ton-per-square-inch pressure at around 4,000 feet. The men are packed together about as closely as the three astronauts in an Apollo moon spaceship.

Since her first 4,000-foot dive, *Deepstar* has made 300 other dives, many to her maximum depth. She has been diving off the coasts of California, Mexico, Panama, Venezuela, Newfoundland, Florida, and the eastern United States.

Men aboard her already have made findings that have contributed to zoology, chemistry, physics, meteorology, geology, geography—the principal sciences that, when applied to the sea, make up oceanography. In her, Kenneth V. Mackenzie, for the Navy's Deep Submergence Group, measures the speed of sound, which varies in the depths.

Once *Deepstar* brought back a surprising specimen from the sea floor. It was surprising in that it did not turn out to be what the crew thought it was.

Poking through the dark water, 750 feet down and barely above the bottom, men aboard *Deepstar* one day thought they saw a remarkable geological specimen.

It appeared to be a black boulder. It was large. It looked like volcanic material. It would be, they thought, an ideal specimen for study—if only they could get it home. Home, in this case, meant to the United States Navy Electronics Laboratory in San Diego, California (today the Navy Undersea Warfare Center, San Diego Division). *Deepstar*, maneuvered by her crew, netted the black chunk with her mechanical arms, held onto it, and placed it in her specimen basket. It was successfully recovered.

Scientists gathered around the black boulder to look at it and analyze it. They found out what it was.

It was a lump of coal. It had probably fallen overboard from a coal-burning ship some time in past years.

Not all the geological specimens brought up from the bottom of the sea are, it seems, rare finds.

Men Under Glass
Under the Sea

16

The greatest mountain range on earth rises from the bottom of the sea. Some time around 1980, men may be living on it. They already are making their plans.

The greatest mountain range is almost all out of sight. Most of its summits are far beneath the surface of the sea—in fact, beneath all the principal seas: the North and South Atlantic, Arctic, Pacific, Antarctic, and Indian oceans.

In the Atlantic it is called the Mid-Atlantic Ridge. It starts around Iceland and Greenland and runs 10,000 miles to the Antarctic Ocean. It is longer than the range of the North American Rocky Mountains and the South American Andes combined. The total length of the world's highest range, the Himalayas, in India, Nepal, and Tibet, is only 1,500 miles, though there are also adjoining ranges that add to that length.

In a few places the summits of the Mid-Atlantic Ridge break the surface. And these are the only places where men have stepped on it, seen it with their own eyes, and lived on it. The Azores Islands are among its peaks. The ridge's Mt. Pico, in the Azores, towers 7,613 feet above the sea and 20,000 feet beneath it, and is almost as tall as Mount Everest (29,028 feet). Ascension Island, a lonely mid-South Atlantic spot where great green turtles lay their eggs, rises out of the ridge. These turtles cross half of the South Atlantic Ocean from Brazil, Archie Carr of the University of Florida has shown, and hit five-mile-long Ascension Island without fail. Other peaks of the ridge in the South Atlantic are St. Peter and St. Paul's rocks, whose surfaces resemble the surface of the moon. From these rocks the nuclear submarine *Triton* started a round-the-world trip submerged, and at these rocks she ended it.

In the far-South Atlantic, the Mid-Atlantic Ridge sends out branches—other mountain ridges on the bottom of the sea—both to the east and to the west. These undersea ranges pass the tips of both Africa and South America and curve into the Pacific and Indian oceans. This worldwide series of mountain ranges is called the Mid-Oceanic Ridge. It stretches altogether a length of 40,000 miles and has an area equal to that of Europe, Asia, and Africa together. Except for the ocean itself, it is the biggest single geographical feature on the earth.

Yet it does not contain the tallest mountain in the world —a peak that rises all alone straight out of the bottom of the sea. The highest mountain is Mauna Kea, Hawaii, 31,000 feet, or almost six miles from the bed of the Pacific to its summit. That's 2,000 feet higher than Mount Everest. Mauna Kea's topmost 13,796 feet extend above the Pacific.

In the western Pacific and the Indian oceans, more mountains of the Mid-Oceanic Ridge rise out of the sea to become islands: the Narcondam Islands in the Indian Ocean, Sumatra, Java, and Timor. In November, 1964, among these East Indian island peaks, the U.S. Coast and Geodetic ship *Pioneer*, commanded by Captain Edward B. Brown, located by echo-sounding a great rift valley framed by some of the undersea mountains. It is the single most important geographic feature on the bottom of the Indian Ocean. It is part of the continuous worldwide rift—a fault, or crack, in the rocky skin of the globe that reaches 45,000 miles.

The undersea mountains run on from Sumatra to Burma; northwest of Rangoon, Burma, the mountains emerge onto dry land to form the eastern Himalayas on the Burma-India border, and then lead up to where the Himalayas reach their highest point, more than five miles above sea level.

The Mid-Atlantic Ridge was first located and some details of it were made known by Britain's *Challenger* expedition of the 1870's. Our knowledge has been extended much further by many of today's oceanographers, in particular by Dr. Maurice Ewing and his associates and graduate students of the Lamont Geological Observatory of Columbia University.

Dr. Ewing describes the undersea mountains: "The ridge in the Atlantic is a median ridge, remaining approximately equidistant from the bordering continents. On a typical trans-Atlantic profile between New England and Spanish Sahara, the Mid-Atlantic Ridge appears as an elevation about one thousand miles wide, reaching about two miles above the basin floor. It is five hundred miles or more across—twice the width of the Andes. It occupies approximately one-third of the whole Atlantic Ocean area, continues through the Indian Ocean, and with alteration of some features, through the southwestern Pacific."

The photos of the Mid-Atlantic Ridge have been revealing. "We spent several days studying a section of the Mid-Atlantic Ridge," said A. S. Laughton of Britain's National Institute of Oceanography, "that huge chain of mountains that runs from Greenland to South Africa down the middle of the Atlantic. When we lowered our cameras onto this ridge, the resulting photographs showed very steep slopes of broken rocks. Especially interesting is the fact that the rocks seem to have been recently disturbed, possibly by an earthquake or an underwater volcanic eruption.

"Other volcanic features are rich in life, the rocks often covered with sponges and corals, and the tall, branching, and very decorative sea fans." Sea fans, also called gorgonians, are animals that are shaped like an opened Japanese fan. They are related to the corals and are common sights, swaying in the currents, in coral reefs near Florida, Bermuda, and the West Indies.

Many of the peaks of the Mid-Atlantic Ridge are 1,000 to 2,000 feet below the surface. Now they can be reached and observed by men in many of today's deep-diving submarines. Trips are being laid out right now to the Mid-Atlantic Ridge for *Aluminaut*. Since *Aluminaut* can dive three miles, she could dive to the base of the ridge.

One plan is to have men living on the ridge—in a round glass house—by about 1980. They will presumably at first live at a high point on the ridge; on or near the summit of a mountain. Undersea mountaineering, a new field just opening today is, you might say, an unusual kind of human activity— in it, you start at the top.

The glass house for the summit beneath the Atlantic is being planned and designed by the Corning Glass Works and by General Electric's Re-Entry Systems Department (a space department). It will be strong enough to protect the men and their instruments inside as far down as 12,000 feet or more. Thus it could be moved or placed lower than a summit, and might occupy a spot in a valley or on a foothill or on a slope of the Mid-Atlantic Ridge.

The glass house will be 12 feet in diameter—in other words, cramped for the two or three men who will live in it, with their equipment. An 18-inch-in-diameter model was to be tested in 1968 at the David Taylor Model Basin, operated by the Naval Ship Research and Development Center.

The 18-inch sphere undergoing testing is made, the Corning Glass people say, of "curved, five-sided segments of glass ceramic material set in a lattice work of titanium framing. Each segment will be about 10 inches in diameter and less than a half-inch thick."

According to Dr. Gail P. Smith of Corning, glass was tried successfully beneath the sea long ago. Dr. Smith quotes Muriel Guberlet's *Explorers of the Sea:* "About 350 B.C., Alexander the Great, wearing his crown and royal robes, is said to have sat on a throne chair under the sea in a barrel made of glass, covered with asses' skins. Under the protection of an angel, and supplied with food, he watched the animals in the deep sea, including a monster so big that it took three days and three nights to swim past the royal observer."

That three-day monster was one of the origins of the stories that persist to this day, of sea serpents.

"At the end of . . . 96 days of his adventure," says *Explorers of the Sea*, "Alexander said, 'The marvelous things of God are exceedingly wonderful.' " Alexander probably was lowered to the shallow sea floor just offshore.

Says the booklet *Little Known Facts About the Submarine* (by General Dynamics/Electric Boat): "Alexander the Great (356 to 323 B.C.), ruler of Macedonia and conqueror of the known world in his time, is the first person known to have descended into the sea in a vessel of any kind." The same booklet quotes a description in a thirteenth-century manuscript that Alexander had glowing lamps inside his barrel. What the lamps would have done to his breathing air is not hard to imagine. And the Middle Ages manuscript, *La Vrai Histoire d'Alexandre*, adds that he saw "many fish that had the form of beasts that live on land and walk on legs . . . and many other wonders that were unbelievable. When Alexander had seen enough . . . he made signs for those above to raise the iron chains and draw him up."

Glass is an ancient material. It has been used by men for thousands of years, so we know Alexander the Great could have used a diving bell of glass. But not until recent times have men known as much as they do about how to use glass.

What we now know has come out of research—research for space and deep-sea projects, among other things. Glass and glass ceramic are strong—they resist pressure; and light—they can float to the surface in any emergency; and they are fail-safe.

Corning's first glass balls for use in the sea were less than an inch in diameter, or about the size of a ping-pong or golf ball. Soon they were 3 inches, then 7 inches, then basketball size, then 24 inches in diameter. Many of the early glass balls were used as floats—to help hold up nets or lines, for example, and as the balls grew in size, the larger ones enclosed oceanographic instruments. Some Corning spheres are Swallow floats, which float at predetermined depths. They are named for their inventor, an English oceanographer, J. C. Swallow.

Glass spheres are so buoyant that they climb to the surface on their own. So they are attached to what is called a free corer. A corer is a length of pipe that in the past has been lowered by line to the sea floor where it is driven into the sediment, sand, or mud, to obtain a sample of the bottom of the sea. A corer by line can take hours to lower—and hours more to raise. A free corer is simply heaved overboard from a ship. No line is used; a weight pulls it down. The free corer goes to the bottom, grabs its sample, drops off the heavy weight that brought it down—and then glass balls attached to it haul it to the surface. There it beeps and flashes a light and is picked up by its ship. The free corer was developed by P. L. Sachs at Woods Hole and by S. O. Raymond of the Benthos Company, a manufacturer of oceanographic equipment at North Falmouth, Massachusetts.

Recent research has affirmed with emphasis that glass under pressure does not crack or shatter. Instead, pressure on the glass simply pushes together the molecules in the glass—and strengthens it. At the Benthos Company, a glass ball under pressure was hit hard by a hardened stainless steel impact pin —a hammer. The glass did not break. The hammer did.

Glass, Corning says, is also rigid and elastic. Under pressure, it slightly changes its shape, it bends, but it doesn't break. When the pressure is removed, it then returns to its original shape.

Glass now is believed to be safe to enclose instruments or men all the way down to a depth of 36,000 feet in the ocean —in other words, to the greatest depths of the sea.

So strong is glass under pressure that it amounts to a new material which would at once suggest itself for use in the hulls of submarines. That is what has occurred. Corning, together with the Navy Ordnance Laboratory, Pennsylvania State University, and Jaroslav P. Stachiw, a scientist, has built a torpedo-shaped, 8-foot-long, 1-foot-in-diameter glass ceramic submarine. It carries only instruments, not men, and is believed to be capable of taking them to a depth of 30,000 feet and returning them safely. It is the first glass ceramic deep-sea vehicle to be constructed.

Other glass submarines are on the way. Corning has drawn plans for a 60-foot-long, 8-foot-in-diameter man-carrying submarine. Her entire bow will be of glass, like a goldfish bowl. A submarine like this, called the *Deep View*, is now being built at the Naval Weapons Center, China Lake, California. *Deep View*, cigar-shaped, will be able to reach a depth of 5,000 feet (about a mile) and is intended mainly to work on the continental shelf beneath the shallow water near the shore. Willis R. Forman, who designed *Deep Jeep*, the 2,000-foot-deep Navy vehicle, is the project manager for *Deep View*. Models of *Deep View* have been tested. The Southwest Research Institute, San Antonio, has built a glass hemisphere to be tested with a completed boat. Hahn and Clay, Incorporated, Houston, are builders of the steel hull. "This," says Forman, "will be the world's first submersible to use glass as part of its pressure hull."

Corning now is preparing to build the 12-foot-in-diameter sphere for the glass house for the Mid-Atlantic Ridge by building bigger and bigger glass spheres. The latest are 44½ inches and 56 inches in diameter. Each size can hold two men.

These big glass balls also are being made into submarines. "The deep submersible of the future," says Harold Bernstein of the Navy's Deep Submergence Systems Project, "may be a glass bubble mounted on an undersea sled with motors and propellers to cruise beneath the surface."

The men will ride inside the bubble, sealed tightly shut. Motors, batteries, and rudders for the submarine will be outside the ball and in or on the pontoons or in a second glass sphere. They may be controlled by light beams, like a flashlight's, operated by the man in the ball. No wires will run from inside out through the glass; they might cause a crack. The light beams will strike photosensitive cells on the pontoons outside the ball and so operate the controls. That at least is the scheme at present, but many details remain to be worked out.

Two glass-ball-and-pontoon submarines are expected to be able to reach the deepest points in the ocean. One of them is called *Hikino*, a Hawaiian word for Can Do. It is being constructed by Donald C. Moore, head of the Astrometrics Division, Weapons Development Department, at the Naval Undersea Warfare Center, Pasadena, California.

The other two-man glass-ball submarine is being built with a private research grant by Dr. William B. McLean, a skin-diving, glasses-wearing scientist who is an idea man for the Navy. He is technical director—that is, research and development boss—at the Naval Undersea Warfare Center.

I asked Dr. McLean to comment on the glass-ball submarine. He wrote:

> Glass in compression is an extremely strong material and at the same time is relatively light in weight. These combined features of strength and lightweight make it theoretically possible to construct underwater vehicles capable of going to the deepest parts of the ocean (36,000 feet) without the large floats of buoyant materials used on the *Trieste* and the other bathyscaphes existing at the present time. For the first time it now appears that a very small glass vehicle could operate at any ocean depth and be able to carry its own support equipment (batteries, ballast etc.) without the need of any buoyancy material outside of that provided by its own hull displacement.

Explorers of the sea will be able to see in all directions in a glass submarine: "A glass hull can provide the omnidirectional viewing so vitally needed by the submersible pilots and scientific observers alike. It can eliminate our present problem of tunnel vision caused by viewports and permit synoptic, multi-directional observations yielding a spacial comprehension never before possible under water."

Dr. McLean hopes to create a glass-ball submarine for about

the cost of a private airplane. He wants as many persons as possible to use it. "If," he says, "we could make the glass bathysphere available so that it can be used individually rather than just by big organizations, there'd be lots more exploration of the bottom."

There are problems in the way of the glass-ball submarine. The glass ball is made in two halves, or hemispheres. These two halves will close like a clam shell and will have to be joined tightly at their equator to protect the men inside. Just how this is going to be done is not yet known.

That all-around visibility is what Dr. McLean sees as the biggest single advantage of glass submarines. "The thing you don't realize about undersea vehicles, until you've been down in one," he says, "is how slowly they move. You just can't turn fast enough to follow a fish or animal. But if you have all-around visibility, as in a glass sphere, you can follow them just by turning your head."

That, presumably, is how Alexander the Great, in his glass diving bell 2,320 years ago, watched the sea serpent that took, he said, three days to pass by him. That may be how, in the future, men inside a glass house and glass submarines will make observations on their journeys to the Mid-Atlantic Ridge or elsewhere on the bottom of the sea.

The Walk
on the
Undersea Peak

17

The first three men to stand on the summit of a mountain beneath the sea gazed around.

"I am sure," said one of them, Dr. Harris B. Stewart, Jr., of the U.S. Coast and Geodetic Survey, "that it looked just as the moon will look to our first men getting there. Hovering about this desolate landscape, knowing that no man had ever been there before, I felt much as our first moon men will feel —excited and very, very much isolated from all the world that we know here on earth."

The other men with him were Dick Rogers and Ensign Paul Larsen of the Cost Survey ship *Pioneer.* The summit of the seamount was below the surface of the South China Sea, west of the Philippine island of Palawan.

The top of the mountain was barren and covered with coarse sand and rubble. "It was an unearthly landscape," Dr. Stewart went on. "But we were not alone, for the top of the seamount held a profusion of small multicolored tropical fish. Generally they seemed to congregate in the isolated patches of luxuriant coral growth, just as Paul and I were drawn to these few 'gardens' in this lunar-like landscape."

Harris Stewart, born in New York in 1922, was one of the first men to get to the ghostly summit of an undersea mountain because he followed what has become the well-beaten trail into oceanography—via the universities and oceanographic institutions. "My real interest in oceanography," he says, "was kindled by Harry Hess at Princeton. We had both gone back there when the war was over." For four years during World War II Stewart had been an Army Air Force pilot in the Pacific. "Hess gave a senior course called, as I recall, 'Special Problems in Geology.' One of these special problems was the guyot or flat-topped seamount problem. He had managed to sneak some science in during his tour as Navigation Officer on the *Cape Johnson* in the South Pacific and had some fine records and interesting hypotheses on these features. I realized that the really stimulating scientific problems in geology were now primarily in marine geology, and this seemed like more fun than mapping quadrangles that probably had already been done. I still had a strong case of wanderlust, and the combination seemed ideally suited to a career in oceanography."

Stewart, brown-eyed, and today a balding 46-year-old, 11 years ago married Elsie Bennett Cunningham of Dedham, Massachusetts. "Her friends," he says, "call her LeeLee." They have a "six-year-old with the standard missing front teeth," he says, "officially Dorothy Cunningham Stewart, she goes by the name of Dodie." Stewart today is director of the Atlantic Oceanographic Laboratories of the Environmental Science Services Administration in Miami, Florida. He takes every precaution with his scuba diving, such as his trip to the undersea summit. "I never had any real scrapes while scuba diving," he says, "not even any close calls. This is due to the excellent training I had under the tutelage of the late Connie Limbaugh at Scripps coupled with an innate caution. There are old divers and bold divers, and I prefer to be identified with the former." Stewart did five years of graduate study in oceanography at

Scripps, and while there became a trained diving geologist. In 1957 he joined the U.S. Coast and Geodetic Survey. In 1965, he became the first head of the Environmental Science Services Administration's Institute of Oceanography.

On the peak of the undersea mountain, Stewart and Larsen set out to collect rocks so Stewart could make geological samplings of them. The men went to the edge of the seamount to dive down along its side and look for rock outcroppings.

"As we approached the edge," Dr. Stewart said, "the color changed from the clear white of reflected sunlight to the dark blue-gray of the deep sea. The edge was abrupt. We could see the sides of the mountain dropping steeply away. It disappeared below us as we swam out over the edge into mile-deep water. We swam down the side for about fifty feet, but found no rock outcrops. As we came back up onto the mountaintop, we felt as though we were back on familiar ground. The 'moonscape' looked much less formidable than the steep side with its eerie light."

The date was March 17, 1964. *Pioneer* at that time was one of the ships on an international expedition to explore the Indian Ocean. *Pioneer* was due over Seahorse Shoal—the location of the seamount—at about 8:30 in the morning. She did not quite get there on time. Dr. Stewart's log tells what happened next:

By 0930 [9:30 A.M.] we thought we had strayed west of the Shoal and turned left to 090 degrees and reduced speed to one-third. Immediately the bottom was observed to shoal from 670 fathoms. Three minutes later it was 240 fathoms and we decided to pull in the magnetometer fish. In two more minutes the depth was 30 fathoms. Lieutenant Commander Barbee raced to the bridge to signal "all stop" just as we heard someone shout "bottom in sight." I went to the starboard wing of the bridge and looked straight down. Alternating dark and light patches appeared to be sliding past the ship. By then the depth reading was 8 fathoms, less than 50 feet of water below keel depth. The bottom had risen

127

like the front of the Empire State Building as we coasted along
in dark shallow water, 66 nautical miles from the nearest land—
Piedras Point on Palawan Island, the westernmost tip of the Philippine Archipelago, bearing 120 degrees. [A nautical mile is 6,080
feet (British Hydrographic Office) or 6,080.20 feet (U.S. Coast
and Geodetic Survey).]

Captain Ed Brown of the *Pioneer*, a veteran of 30 years
with the Coast Survey, asked Dr. Stewart, who was chief
scientist aboard, if he would like to dive to the mountaintop
beneath the sea. Stewart, as soon as he had determined that the
undersea currents were not so strong as to forbid diving, said
he would. His log relates:

I was equipped with the following items for the dive: Geology
hammer, collecting bag, wrist compass, leg knife, watch, writing
slate, inflatable life preserver, tanks, fins, and mask. The other
two divers had similar equipment. Larsen and I stayed under and
Rogers popped up to the surface to get his camera—a French
Calypso with flash—from the tending boat. Then we all met at
about 20 feet, checked our watches, and headed for the bottom
so wonderfully visible in the warm clear water some 30 feet
below us.

Once on the bottom, we could see the full 311 feet of the
Pioneer above us, and horizontally the visibility was a good 200
feet. We saw no rock other than coral and algae, but there was
lots of that. This was not the luxuriant reef type of Swan Island
in the Caribbean, but more open, with more coral rubble and
isolated patches of intense and varied growth.

The topography was gently rolling with occasional NW-SE
trending broad gentle swales. Flat and slightly meandering valleys
between the swales might not have been noticed if it had not
been for the deposits of white sands and gravels in these valleys.
These deposits were made up of coral detritus, some *Halimeda*
segments, and lots of the big coral reef foraminifera (marginu-
lina?).

The three men collected biological specimens. "The specimens were beautiful indeed," said Stewart. "There were occasional crinoids. The two I collected for the sack were about 8

inches high and had perhaps 50 feathery arms each. One was a brilliant yellow, the other was black and white."

The crinoids, one of the most unusual animals in the sea, are the sea lilies. They have long stalks that anchor to the sea floor. Atop each stalk is a body shaped like a globe—or like a lily. From the body, there grow many plumelike arms which branch open to sweep small organisms into the crinoid's mouth. They are a deep-water animal, rarely seen. They were more common in the Paleozoic era than today. Their fossils, stone lilies, are the chief constituent of many beds of limestone.

The flower-like crinoids are echinoderms; they are related to sea urchins, starfish, brittle stars, sea cucumbers, and sand dollars.

"One holothurian (*Sticophus?*) measured two feet long and a good 5 inches in diameter. It was a brilliant red, but lost both its shape and color once it was aboard ship and placed in formalin."

Most holothurians—sea cucumbers—are dull green or brown. Most are small (a few inches to a foot); in the West Indies, Arctic, Antarctic, and on Australia's Great Barrier Reef the cucumber-shaped animals reach 5 or 6 feet long and become thick as a man's thigh. With their flexible bodies, they creep over the bottom. On the Great Barrier, the sea cucumber feeds on big pieces of coral; after the coral polyp is digested, the remaining limestone is ejected. When it is frightened, the sea cucumber turns itself inside out—it protrudes its internal organs. A remarkable animal at replacing its own missing parts, the sea cucumber can grow new internal organs—and can even grow another body. In the Orient men call the sea cucumber delicious; one American girl, Mary Lombardi, who sampled it, found it rubbery. I thought it was like the salt pork in pork and beans, only tougher. My wife says that although the flavor is not objectionable, the texture would take some getting used to. William Beebe, 300 feet down, found a new species of yellow-green sea cucumber. Sea cucumbers are common in tide pools, under rocks, in sand and mud and on the bottom of the deep sea, 12,000 feet and farther down. Gilbert

C. Klingel in *The Bay* reported something I never have seen reported elsewhere: He saw the calm, sunny surface of the Caribbean once covered by a vast assemblage of contentedly wriggling sea cucumbers. When the wind came and waves churned up, they instantly sank out of sight.

Dr. Stewart continued in his log:

Some really fine corals were collected, some of which should end up in the museum back in Washington. By the time our dive was over, Rogers had shot some 24 of his 36 shots with the camera.

After the planned 30 minutes, we started up with the three of us pulling on the bag [the collecting bag] which weighed about 100 pounds by then. My pockets were filled with sediment samples and we just could not get up. We unhooked our lifebelts, fastened them to the top of the bag, and inflated them. This provided just enough buoyancy, and we broke the surface just 34 minutes after we began the dive. The boat towed us to the ship where we used the diving ladder to bridge the gap between the bottom of the starboard Jacob's ladder and the water surface, which now had 4-to-5-foot waves.

Men from the *Pioneer* made a second scuba dive at Invisible Bank off the Andaman Islands on April 17, 1964. In nine to ten fathoms, they found turbid water, baseball-sized algal balls, small yellowfin tuna, red snapper, colorful tropical fish, and a barracuda. When a shark swam up, the three divers climbed the Jacob's ladder as one man—and ended the dive.

Since the *Pioneer's* visit to Seahorse Shoal, men have reached the peaks of other undersea mountains: They have been down to Cobb Seamount off the coast of the state of Washington, and to the Vema Seamount in the South Atlantic. "So far as we know," Dr. Stewart says, "the trip we made down to the top of a seamount in the South China Sea was the first time man had ever been on top of an undersea mountain. Having climbed mountains on land, I know that this is by far the easier way to get to the top."

The Disappearing
Seamount

18

The skipper of *American Scout* was puzzled. His echo-sounder showed there was only 20 fathoms (120 feet) of water beneath the keel of his ship.

He was at 46° 20′ North and 37° 21′ West. That is, he was in mid-ocean, on a perfectly well-charted North Atlantic shipping lane, a lane so heavily traveled by ships that they form almost a parade across the ocean.

The captain had ordered that his echo-sounder be switched on after personnel on the bridge had noticed an unusual green color in the ocean.

The echo-sounder at once recorded that depth of only 120 feet and continued to register the same depth for ten minutes. Then contact with the bottom—or what seemed to be the bottom—was lost.

American Scout did not drop a lead line over her side to verify the depth figure provided by the Fathometer. There appeared to be no reason to do so.

A reading of 120 feet and then a dropoff suggests, clearly enough, that the ship has passed over the top of a mountain that rises from the bottom, and whose sides are steep. Such readings have been obtained by naval and merchant and ocean-ographic vessels from many places in the seas. The use of echo-sounders has increased until today many ships are equipped with them, and actually millions of new depth readings are obtained from the oceans each year. These readings are forwarded to the Naval Oceanographic Office in Washington, D.C. When verified, they are incorporated into the pilot charts that are published, 32 million a year, by the Naval Oceanographic Office (NavOceanO for short) for the use of ships all over the seven seas.

NavOceanO, the former Hydrographic Office, was founded 137 years ago by Matthew Fontaine Maury. Today, it is housed in 23 buildings in Washington, D.C. It controls 27 ships and 4 airplanes. It employs more oceanographers perhaps than any other organization.

The story of the *American Scout* seamount was the subject of an informal manuscript, *Non-Existent Seamounts—A Case Study*, by Joseph G. Gilg and James J. McConnell, Jr., of NavOceanO, which appeared in September, 1966.

Once he had obtained his reading of an only 120-foot shallow depth in what was supposedly the deep ocean, the skipper of *American Scout* awaited verification—a similar figure from another vessel in the same area of ocean.

He immediately got it.

But soon thereafter, when other ships went out to locate the seamount exactly—for purposes of charting—they could not find it. They have not found it to this day. The *American Scout* seamount became a vanishing seamount—or was it non-existent in the first place?

American Scout first discovered the seamount—or what was supposed to be a seamount—in July, 1948. The verification at approximately the same place was by *American Scientist*, and a month later, using her Fathometer, she located the seamount again. She said she found the summit 120 feet deep at 46° 23′ North and 37° 20′ West.

This time an attempt was made to check by lead line, but no bottom was reached with it.

Another ship obtained the most extensive sounding of the *American Scout* seamount that very same month of August, 1948. The S.S. *Southland's* Fathometer showed soundings of 29, 29, 32, 90, and 35 fathoms (a fathom is 6 feet) between 46° 18′ North and 37° 45′ West and 40° 20′ North and 37° 38′ West. No soundings at all were recorded on the Fathometer, the Gilg and McConnell manuscript says, either before or after the recording of the shallow depths. The *Southland* did not report dropping a lead line.

Sixteen years after the *American Scout*, the *American Scientist*, and the *Southland*, the seamount was reported again.

This time, in July, 1964, the S.S. *Wacosta* found a 19-fathom depth at 40° 06′ North and 38° 01′ West. This depth, says NavOceanO, was recorded for one minute of sailing time. There was no trace of the shallow depth either before or after that minute. No use of lead line was reported.

The evidence seemed clear enough: Repeated Fathometer readings showed the approximate location of a new seamount beneath the open Atlantic.

All that remained, a simple enough and routine process, was to pinpoint it exactly for navigational charts. Locating seamounts is important to navigation. If you are a ship captain and know exactly where a seamount is, then when your Fathometer reflects sound from it, you also know exactly where you are. Locating seamounts also has become more and more important as more and more submarines cruise the seas at depths at which they could conceivably strike uncharted seamounts. No submarine yet has been known to have run into a submerged peak. But it could happen.

Seamounts these days actually are discovered and proved to be real, with astonishing frequency. Late in 1966, the Department of Commerce published six new maps of the sea floor around the Aleutian Islands, off Alaska. The maps included information gathered by the Coast and Geodetic Survey between 1943 and 1964. They show dozens of previously uncharted undersea mountains, mountain ridges, canyons, and sea basins in the Bering Sea and in the North Pacific. One of the newly found seamounts rises 6,510 feet, or well over a mile, from the bottom of the sea, and was named for the late Rear Admiral K. T. Adams, once assistant director of the Coast and Geodetic Survey.

In 1960, the Coast and Geodetic Survey found an unsuspected seamount summit within 90 feet of the surface of the Caribbean. The Bermuda islands are the tops of isolated mountains—not part of an undersea ridge—that reach from the sea floor to above the surface.

Naval or oceanographic ships could easily, it appeared, verify the location of the *American Scout* seamount. They couldn't. They couldn't find the seamount. They haven't found it yet.

In 1958, the British oceanographic vessel *Discovery II* was in the general area. She looked for the seamount. Instead, she got on her Fathometer a minimum depth of 2,362 fathoms. No shallow water at all.

In 1961, the U.S.S. *Harder*, crossing within three miles of the shallow soundings reported by *Southland*, got a minimum depth of 2,450 fathoms. The *Harder's* Fathometer report showed the bottom to be relatively flat—no seamount there at all.

In 1962, the U.S.S. *Yakutat* crossed the area about six miles south of the *American Scout* and *Wacosta* soundings. She got minimum depths of 2,200 and 2,300 fathoms. She got depths of at least 100 fathoms shallower than any other soundings in the area, "indicating," say Gilg and McConnell, "a consistent depth error in the record."

In 1964, the research vessel *Atlantis II* crossed the area looking for the *American Scout* seamount. *Atlantis II*, operated by Woods Hole, is one of the United States' newest and best equipped oceanographic vessels.

She found a minimum depth of 2,375 fathoms between the positions of the *American Scout* sounding and the *Southland* soundings, and an average depth of 2,420 fathoms.

In 1965, the United States Naval Oceanographic Office sent out its own ship, the U.S.N.S. *Gilliss*, to resolve the mystery. She conducted both a sounding and magnetic survey. Her soundings indicated a general depth of 2,420 fathoms— right where the undersea peak was supposed to be.

Her magnetic survey failed to find an anomaly (a deviation) that would indicate the presence of a seamount. "Smoothness of the magnetic field," Gilg and McConnell explain, "indicates that the magnetic sources are relatively deep."

Next, the U.S.N.S. *Silas Bent*, another Naval Oceanographic Office vessel, surveyed the area. The *Silas Bent*, launched in 1964, was at the time the Navy's latest oceanographic ship. (A sister ship, the U.S.N.S. *Elisha Kane*, joined the Navy in 1967.) The *Silas Bent* made her trip to the area of the *American Scout* seamount in June, 1966. She found no depth less than 2,362 fathoms.

The *Silas Bent* completes the record to date: Four ships have taken echo-sounder readings indicating a seamount; six research and/or naval vessels have been unable to find the seamount anywhere in the reported area.

Why not?

It may be because it isn't there.

Could an undersea object as big as a seamount have been missed by naval and oceanographic ships? Authors Gilg and McConnell do not think so. A seamount generally is 10 to 12 times wider than it is high, so its contours, or slopes or sides, would show up as a change in depth over a pretty long line. "The concentration of sounding data now available for the [*American Scout* seamount] area," say Gilg and McConnell, "makes it highly unlikely that a feature of this magnitude would not be detected."

The failure of the magnetic survey of the *Gilliss* to find a magnetic anomaly is still more evidence that the mountain is not there.

There is a reason why merchant ships sometimes report shallow depths while oceanographic and naval ships do not. Merchant ships are usually equipped with sounding equipment for shallow water—such as is encountered when entering or leaving port. Such shallow-water sounding gear sometimes records shallow depths when actually the ship is over deep water. A reason is that a mysterious layer returns echoes to ship's echo-sounders.

Ever since World War II, sailors have been bothered by echo-sounder charts that showed what look like very shallow depths where the scientists are positive the sea is deep.

Echo-sounding came into widespread use during World War II. Naval ships sent sound impulses into the sea; the echoes bounced back from the bottom or from enemy submarines. They also bounced back from some whales, with the result that the whales got depth-charged. They bounced back from—and the sound was scattered by—something unknown. There was a layer of something, a few hundred feet down, in midwater and not on the bottom, that returned the sound.

Many theories have been proposed as to what the deep scattering layer, or DSL, as it is called, may be. The deep scattering layer climbs upward through the water at night, from as far as 900 feet down all the way up to the surface or near it, a vertical rise that suggests the layer is made up of animal and fish life that can climb. A rise of 900 feet (almost the height of the Empire State Building) would appear to be an incredible regular rise for what may be small animals or fish, and so the rise of the deep scattering layer may be one of the wonders of the oceans. At any rate, men have tried to sample the layer. They have caught some fish from it; they have caught some plankton from it; they have sampled the water in it. Is the DSL plankton? Probably some of the DSL is plankton. Fish? Probably, including lantern fish. A lantern fish contains, as do many other fish, a gas bubble that reflects and scatters sound from sonar instruments. Squid? Probably squid are in the layer. Jacques-Yves Cousteau calls the deep scattering layer "the mystery of the century."

The marine animals in the deep scattering layer were observed personally by Dr. Eric Barham of the United States Navy Electronics Laboratory in the bathyscaphe *Trieste* and in Cousteau's diving saucer.

Dr. Barham made four trips to about the saucer's limit of

1,000 feet. He told about them in *Science*, Volume 151, March 18, 1966. He saw myctophids (lantern fish), small fishes that normally live deep but are known to climb upward, as does the scattering layer, at night. The lantern fish have numerous light-producing organs along their bodies. Dr. Barham also saw physonects, or siphonophores; these jellyfish-like creatures possess an air-filled float that reflects sound. Dr. Barham noted that the maximum migration rate upward and downward of the deep scattering layer was about 12 meters (39 feet) a minute. The siphonophores moved faster down than up, he observed.

Off San Diego, in *Trieste*, Dr. Barham observed the scattering layer at the depth where sonar sets on the surface showed it to be. Again, he found lantern fish and siphonophores. This suggests a film of jellyfish-like animals spread beneath the surface of all oceans—quite a picture. "I think," Dr. Barham says, "this is true in some ocean areas, but not all." Other scattering-layer animals may be the hatchet fish and the euphausiid shrimp, the krill gulped by the biggest whales.

What the DSL is may finally be determined by deep-diving submarines following a method that was outlined to me by Dick Usry, the pilot of *Deepstar 4000*. "We made three dives in twenty-four hours into the deep scattering layer," Usry said. We went into the layer where the Fathometer on our mother ship said it was. Then we sat in the middle and rose with the layer as it rose to the surface." Men aboard *Deepstar* saw shrimp. Her slurper sucked in samples of the water—its small animal and plant life—for analysis later. It will take a good many dives like this to identify all the animals in the layer because they probably vary in different areas of the sea.

Aboard *Alvin*, Woods Hole scientists dived into the deep scattering layer off Cape Hatteras, North Carolina. They found, *Naval Research Reviews* in January, 1968, reported, "layers of squid, myctophid-like fish, and euphausiids, each comprising a reflecting layer."

On October 3-6, 1967, off Woods Hole, *Alvin* dived with lights off into a mysterious something known as Alexander's

Acres that scatters sound in continental slope water. *Alvin* used her sonar. At range "zero" she switched on her lights. She was in the midst of a school of thousands and thousands of lantern fish. Pilot Marvin J. McCamis drove the submarine through the school and caught dozens of lantern fish in a special net rigged on *Alvin's* sampling basket. Other dives to Alexander's Acres brought the same result: lantern fish.

The deep scattering layer has been called a blanket of life beneath the surface. It does not necessarily require a blanket of animals to provide the echoes we get, Dr. Richard H. Backus of Woods Hole, who has worked on the layer, says. The animals in the layer could be spaced fairly far apart.

As a result of the DSL, shallow reefs have been reported in many locations, particularly in the Pacific Ocean, where there is actually no such thing as a reef. Similarly, there may be no seamounts where some have been indicated.

If the DSL is present, and it has by now been reported in most all areas of the oceans, it is possible that its echo will be interpreted as the true bottom.

"A scattering layer," say Gilg and McConnell, "is indicated in the vicinity of the *American Scout* seamount from several bits of evidence. The S.S. *American Scientist* could not find bottom with a lead line while recording shallow depths on the Fathometer. The *Atlantis II* mentions the presence of a scattering layer while approaching the area (Backus and Worthington, 1965). Personnel of the S.S. *American Scout* mention an odd green color to the water which subsequently does not appear to have been a true bottom. A scattering layer is most conclusively identified on the echo-sounder record of the U.S.N.S. *Silas Bent.*" The *Silas Bent* got a strong return from a scattering layer just below 180 feet down, a light trace from a deeper scattering layer, and the bottom trace at 2,400 fathoms.

From all the evidence, Gilg and McConnell concluded, "the *American Scout* seamount does not exist in the location reported unless it is an unusually steep sided feature which does not possess significant magnetic character." This, they point out, is unlikely.

Someday a new tool, such as a space satellite—or explorations by a deep-diving submarine—may decide exactly where the *American Scout* seamount is, or if it exists at all.

The solution? The Naval Oceanographic Office no longer contours a seamount here. But on its charts the shallow soundings are retained. There is a notation: "Existence doubtful."

19

A deep-diving submarine keeps a log of each undersea journey.

TIME	DEPTH IN METERS	
1350	surface	Launch
1355	surface	Submerged
1402	229	Color changing from blue to purple
1403	268	Color change from deep purple to blue black
	300	Six foot thresher shark observed by pilot.

Marvin McCamis of Woods Hole was the pilot who, peering through the viewport into the blue-black sea, saw the shark. He was driving the *Alvin* on her Dive 200.

She was diving to the southern edge of the manganese pavement area of the Blake Plateau. She was following up *Aluminaut's* trip to the same area on the bottom of the sea. *Alvin* was off Georgia; her exact location was 31° 18′ North and 78° 53′ West. The date was July 4, 1967.

TIME	DEPTH IN METERS	
1410		Approaching bottom: Much suspended matter (snow) in water.
1426	535	Reached bottom.

There were a few small manganese nodules visible. The bottom was globigerina sand. There was no natural light. The *Alvin* drifted with the current to the north at 62 centimeters a second.

She had left West Palm Beach, Florida, at noon July 2 aboard her mother ship *Lulu* with an escort ship, *Humble*.

Now she was in the Gulf Stream—the current that moved her north. Along with McCamis, senior pilot, were copilot Valentine Wilson and R. M. Pratt of Virginia Polytechnic Institute as observer.

"We landed on a smooth to very gently rolling bottom," the trip report said, "with numerous ripple marks and occasional scour marks around obstructions. Throughout the dive this was the characteristic topography."

TIME	DEPTH IN METERS	
1429	531	White to light sand bottom. Not as much snow near bottom as further up in water column.
1437		Attempting to get on bottom and hold. Finally held with lift prop and main prop both going. Current 50 cm/sec from 150° to 180°.

"The most interesting aspect of Dive 200, was the current on the bottom," the report continued. The current is measured by a Savonius rotor mounted on *Alvin's* conning tower; its revolutions are read in knots on a meter inside the submarine. The direction of the current is determined by eyesight or from the heading of the submarine. In the current, everything seemed to be moving. "Hydroids and sponges oscillated in the current and fish were pointed upstream. Everywhere sand and debris was moving along the bottom. Sand ripples were in active motion and large sponges and rocks had scour depression around their bases, and lee side accumulations behind them. . . . The only place with no active motion on the bottom was [a] depression but here the sediment was very coarse loose sand suggesting recent filling."

TIME	DEPTH IN METERS	
539	1439	Sitting on bottom and trying to recover small slab. Water temperature 14° C. Globigerina sand with active ripples. Lee side accumulations behind sponges and coral, and scour depressions around the obstructions.
1515		Trying to pick up nodules. Several 20-30 centimeter nodules in front of the sub. Rat-tail fish. Numerous small corals and sponges, 6 to 10 centimeters high. Nothing large. Little swirls of sediment everywhere and constant sand movement. Sessile growth in constant motion. [Sessile means attached by the base.]
1525	543	Give up on attempt to recover a nodule. Current 25 to 35 centimeters a second from 160 to 180°. Rippled ooze all the way.
1532	543	3-cm reddish crab. Bottom completely rippled.
1536	543	Stop on bottom. Retrieve 10 cm piece of indurated [hardened] ooze. Iridescent greenish fish heading into current. Small amount of snow.

"The most surprising aspect of the dive was the abundance of life on the bottom," said the trip report. "Everywhere we worked, fish and crabs were visible. Most of the fish were small (5-10 centimeters) and had a density of about 1 per 25 to 50 m². One large (40-50 cm) grouper-like fish swam around the submarine for about 10 minutes . . . a 1-meter mottled dogfish was seen on the bottom.

"Sessile life was always in evidence on bottom but was never really abundant. Large sponges and various hydroids were the dominant forms; other organisms included crinoids, gorgonians, echinoids, and a big round, red sponge."

TIME	DEPTH IN METERS	
1540	543	Pick up water sample 1, and sand core. Photographing a large 40-50 cm grouper-like fish which is swimming around the submarine. Large (20-30 cm high) calcarenite mounds on the bottom.

With the grouper in the right place (fish rarely pose that helpfully), it could be photographed with a stereo-mounted pair of Edgerton cameras on the other forward hull. The rest of the time the three men in the *Alvin* poked a movie camera and 35-millimeter still cameras at the viewports and shot their pictures through the viewports. This saves the *Alvin's* battery power and even gets good pictures in poor light.

TIME	DEPTH IN METERS	
1614	542	Driving to west. Can't stop on bottom without reversing props. Current 75 cm/sec from 180.
1635		Large manganese slabs and broken pavement. Occasional sponge and coral on the manganese; manganese shows black and stark against the sand background. Manganese forms ridge of some linear extent as observed and also recorded on sub sonar."

Aluminaut had found a smooth manganese pavement on the Blake Plateau and had rolled over it on wheels attached beneath her hull.

The *Alvin* on Dive 200 instead found large slabs of broken pavement. The large manganese slabs reached up to 3 or 5 meters in maximum size. "A few slabs appeared cracked and broken, and at one place slabs seemed to be piled upon each other." After a lot of work the *Alvin* picked up a slab that seemed to be embedded in the bottom. The slab went into her sample basket and was brought up. Today it is Woods Hole Oceanographic Institution Sample 2700.

TIME	DEPTH IN METERS	
1644	547	Sitting on bottom in depression. Coarse sand to gravel with much broken coral and pteropods [the sea snails that swim with wings] in the sediment. No ripples, some possible dunes, no sessile life. Sediment seems to fill the shallow depression; *Alvin* skid tracks reveal loose sand, 5-10 centimeters deep. Collected water sample 2.

The Alvin found the bottom sediment and rocks much like those expected from earlier dredge hauls and photographs.

TIME	DEPTH IN METERS	
1715	546	Trying to pick up manganese nodule on bottom globigerina sand with 8-10 cm long ripples; dunes in distance with 3-5 m wave length and large sponges in holes.
1725		Picked up 20 cm manganese nodule. Sample tray full. Proceed toward the west on course 200. Large 10-cm round sponge under submarine.
1745	542	Dropped ascent weight and start for surface. As soon as we left bottom the snow started.
1802	168	Zone of salps in water, and numerous live Globigerina (?). [Salps are transparent, barrel-shaped tunicates; they join together to make chains.]
1804	100	Very blue water; clear to surface
1809	Surface	

Thus ended the *Alvin's* first dive to the Blake Plateau. Three others followed immediately.

On Dive 201, to 555 meters, her men—Dr. Frank Manheim of the United States Geological Survey was the observer; McCamis and Wilson, the pilots—saw the bottom covered with "dark nodules, at first small and pebbly, but some larger lumps, cobbles, and then slabs appeared." Dark sediment proved chiefly glauconite with small phosphorite grains. The men reached and photographed an outcropping shelf of silty limestone whose end they could not see. They found large brown-black boulders 2 to 3 meters wide, "probably consisting of manganese and iron-impregnated phosphorite."

Dive 201's trip report stated:

Only one large fish, a 1½-meter Mako shark was observed. [He] was resting on or near bottom and raised a cloud of sediment when he was aroused by the submersible and flashed past.

The most common small fish appeared to be small deep-sea eels, dull brownish-buff with poorly marked mouth and eyes (frequently not evident at all), 6-20 cm in length. They moved very slowly and often rested near or on the bottom with their bodies curved around a nodule or projection from the bottom. Small skates the same size were somewhat less common, followed by half-dollar-sized hatchetfish *(Sternoptyx)*. These bright, silvery forms seemed to frequent water about 4-6 meters or more above the bottom, darting straight downward at a speed of 1/3 meter a second and moving back up again without stopping. Other fish seen included rat-tailed fish *(morids);* red snappers; several red, bass-like fish about 20 cm long; silvery, goldfish-like fish having a rapid (8 m/sec) darting motion when disturbed, and a golden pouched fish with antenna-like projections below and above the jaw *(Chaunax)*. This specimen was half buried in the mud before being disturbed.

The men saw a "stubby, varicolored-splotched fish ranging from greenish fluorescent to pink." It was 9 centimeters long, and it hung motionless on the bottom.

The men also saw other small fish, large and small crabs, snails, squid, spiny urchins, sea cucumbers, shrimplike creatures, octopus, starfish and a few brittle stars. At around 555 meters down, that must be about the deepest an octopus was ever observed.

Some fish and crabs were not disturbed by the *Alvin* till she got quite close.

"Deep water corals (*Lophelia* and *Dendrophyllia*)," the trip report says, "[along with] alcyonarian corals, hydroids, sponges and bryozoans typically grew out from the tips of hard surfaces such as the phosphate manganese slabs." The undersides of the slabs were occupied by worms, siliceous sponges, and unidentified gelatinous growths.

The men again saw snow, or suspended matter, in the water—mostly "unrecognizable or irregular aggregates, flocs, or blobs." When the *Alvin's* descent slowed, they could make out living zooplankton. They found snow barely beneath the surface; it was increasing at 16 meters; and it reached all the way to just above the bottom at 523 meters.

On the bottom at 554.3 meters, they saw "masses of flea-like organisms [that] move in jerks every few seconds."

On Dive 202, with E. F. K. Zarudski of Woods Hole as observer—the dive on which the *Alvin* was attacked by a swordfish—the three men aboard her saw snow "from the surface to about 40 meters above the bottom. At 470 meters a sardine-like fish and a small jellyfish appeared. At 560 meters a ribbon-like fluorescent creature 8 inches long, ¾ inches wide, undulated past the window."

On Dive 203, with J. O. Milliman of Woods Hole as observer, the *Alvin*, on the western edge of the Blake Plateau, found on the bottom crescent-shaped, meandering dunes inside a series of ridges and troughs. Deepwater branching corals lived atop the ridges. So did anemones and alcyonarians. "Orange brittle stars," the trip report says, "lived in corals, locally in high concentrations, greater than 100 individuals/m²." Large (greater than 20 centimeters across) spider crabs maneuvered on the bottom. "Compared to the ridges, the troughs seemed like a desert, contained mottled dogfish but few other creatures." In the troughs, "Tiny bugs, similar to beach flea amphipods, were seen flitting about the bottom."

Then came a surprise:

"Prior to the dive," says observer Milliman, "pilot McCamis baited a hook and attached it to the sled. On the trough bottom, when the line was grasped by the mechanical arm and the bait wriggled, the previously barren trough bottom began to come alive.

"Several crabs came up and tried to devour the bait. Several fish appeared but were chased away by the crabs. The speed with which these mobile animals were able to respond to the baited hook makes me believe they were close by, perhaps in hiding from the *Alvin*. Thus any estimate of mobile animals seen on the bottom may not be accurate since the animals may initially hide when the *Alvin* approaches."

On the *Alvin's* Dive 204, July 13, 1967, the men aboard were McCamis, Manheim, and Milliman. *Alvin* had left the Blake Plateau and was on the continental slope north of Cape Hatteras, North Carolina. Her men found the upper slope very steep—greater than 70 degrees.

Right at the start of Dive 204, the *Alvin's* men off Hatteras once again saw snow: "Gelatinous flocs and blobs of suspended matter up to 1½ cm in diameter." They saw jellyfish the same size as the large flocs of suspended matter.

At 277 meters, the *Alvin* left the Gulf Stream—by dropping beneath it.

On this trip, the *Alvin* dived to where sonar on the surface had shown deep scattering layers. Something unknown was scattering and reflecting sound back to the surface. What was it? The *Alvin* ran out of the light zone at 157 meters. Soon she found: (1) layers of squid, 215 to 253 meters down, and again at 570 meters; the squid squirted yellow ink at her; (2) layers of minnow-like silvery-colored lantern fish at 253 to 350 meters and at 570 and 610; and, (3) another layer of another species of fish, 3 to 7 centimeters long, at 614 to 660 meters. "Small (1½ to 5 cm) transparent shrimplike crustaceans with red-orange-colored organs and large antennae," the report of Dive 204 says, "were present in large concentrations between depths of 370 and 510 meters." Neither shrimp nor squid have air bladders to reflect sound. The *Alvin's* trip report has a surprise, therefore: "It is concluded that while these animals might be numerically dominant in scattering layers, they do *not* represent the actual sound scatterers."

"In the middle of each layer," the trip report explains, "populations were almost exclusively of one species, but at the peripheries populations were mixed. . . . The distribution of squid, fish and shrimp correspond[s] closely with the depths of the strong and two weak reflecting layers."

The *Alvin* found "necklace-like animals" at a number of depths.

She passed through a school of small fish (2 to 5 centimeters long) so thick her men could see only 1½ feet out their viewports. "After several minutes of driving just above the bottom, we passed out of their school." The most common bottom fish off Hatteras were a flat, solelike fish 8 to 15 centimeters long, and a slow-moving, silver-colored eel-like fish 3 to 20 centimeters long. Worm tubes stuck out of the bottom. "Some were white, straight tubes, sticking out of the mud bottom, others were slime-covered, hooplike tubes. Some polychaetes [worms] were seen extending from their tubes but for the most part no sign of life was seen.

"Near the bottom populations of small (less than 2 cm long), shrimplike crustaceans were seen swimming in the water, occasionally resting on the bottom.

"Flat fish move slowly over the bottom in starts and stops possibly causing many of the tracks we see." The bottom at 667 meters is described in the trip report: "Gooey mud."

There was more snow to the bottom. The *Alvin* found steep walls, indicating a box canyon, but had to end the dive before her men could explore it.

Heavy weather set in, as it is likely to do off Cape Hatteras. On the ascent, the snow-suspended matter seemed to vary directly, as did the plankton and nekton (the active swimmers). "This suggests either a causal relationship (plankton and nekton are attracted to suspended matter), or an effect (plankton and nekton produce, probably by defecation, much of the suspended material)."

Lulu took the *Alvin* aboard, and *Lulu* and *Humble* sailed to Little Creek, Virginia. The *Alvin's* 1967 explorations off the Southeast Coast of the United States were over. Her findings will be studied and analyzed for years to come.

The Cave in the Sea Floor

20

The cave started as a huge hole in the bottom of the sea. Peering into the entrance from a tiny submarine, Dr. Francis Parker Shepard could see the sandy floor of the cave slope downward and out of sight.

There was not room enough inside the cave for the submarine, Jacques-Yves Cousteau's diving saucer, to enter. So wherever the cave goes is unknown. It could have an exit lower down than its entrance. Nobody knows. Dr. Shepard, professor of submarine geology at Scripps, does not know what made the cave. It could have been a block that fell down from a canyon wall above.

Dr. Shepard, in the diving saucer, was exploring San Lucas Canyon near the far tip—the southern end—of Lower California. Diving as far as 1,020 feet, he found ripple marks in the sandy floor that indicate currents. He found that the currents change—they reverse directions, like the tide, and do not flow one way, like a river. On one day he found no current.

Dr. Shepard saw that steep slopes formed the sides of San Lucas Canyon. Below 850 feet, Dr. Shepard saw great blocks of granite that had tumbled down from the canyon's walls.

In the saucer, Dr. Shepard explored also Scripps Canyon, in the Pacific floor, just offshore from the Scripps Institution in La Jolla. "One of the great difficulties in the exploration of the geology of the sea floor," said the geology professor, "has been our inability to go down and look at the bottom." Now he could. He had known from wire soundings that Scripps Canyon had precipitous rocky walls. "But we were amazed," he said, "to find that the narrow ravines with vertical and even overhanging walls, found at the head by scuba divers, extend virtually the entire length of the canyon. In the portion where the axis is about seven hundred feet deep, there are sections so narrow that the nine-foot-wide saucer cannot descend to the bottom. At one place, I looked down on converging walls of rock with a gap of about five feet, through which I could see a wider sandy bottom beneath.

"Coming up from some of our dives, we repeatedly had to push off with the mechanical arm to get out from under the overhangs. Bumps were not infrequent, and the outer hull of the saucer became dented from encounters with the rocky walls of this and other canyons."

As off Lower California, Dr. Shepard found currents running up and down in Scripps Canyon—sometimes so strong that the diving saucer with its ½-knot speed, could not sail against them. He again found fallen blocks of granite from the canyon walls in the sediment on the bottom. He found these blocks being moved slowly down the canyon—that is, out toward sea—by an unknown force that Dr. Shepard calls "some active process." Said he at a research meeting at Bristol, England, "How much significance our discoveries may have is yet too early to predict, but they give plenty of incentive for further exploration, especially at greater depths."

The cave in the bottom of the sea is one of the recent discoveries men have made either on the bottom of the sea or in its depths. Other examples:

A fish with three legs like a milking stool. An odd number of legs (not an even two or four) is a rare thing for an animal. Legs—any number—are rare on a fish. We know of the tripod fish only because men in a bathyscaphe saw it. Georges Houot of France commented: "At seven thousand feet we saw a benthosaurus for the first time in its own habitat." It was sitting there, on long, stiltlike legs (or leglike fins) that keep it above the muck on the sea floor. The men in the bathyscaphe, Houot and Commander Philippe Tailliez, took the benthosaurus' picture and brought the photo back to prove what they had seen. The three legs, or stilts, may be doing something else besides holding up the fish: They may be probing the mud for worms or other food.

A triangle-shaped fish. At 3,000 feet down in the bathyscaphe *F.N.R.S. 3*, Jacques-Yves Cousteau saw a "red-and-white fish about five inches long. I switched the light on and recognized shrimps with bodies completely stretched out, their multiple legs jerking." Then he saw an animal never previously reported: "Entering my field of vision . . . was a fish twenty inches long and shaped exactly like a draftsman's triangle. It was the shade and thinness of aluminum foil with a ridiculous little tail."

Clues to aluminum. Clifford A. Kaye of the United States Geological Survey reports that pebbles of bauxite (an ore of aluminum) have been discovered in glacial debris at Martha's Vineyard, Massachusetts. He says the original source of the pebbles was the southward movement of ice thousands of years ago. "This may mean," says Kaye, "that undiscovered bauxite deposits exist in places beneath the Atlantic Coastal Plain."

A previously unknown current. At a UNESCO conference, Dr. Thomas S. Austin of the United States Bureau of Commercial Fisheries (he is now Director of the National Oceanographic Data Center) reported on an Atlantic undersea current. It had originally been mentioned by Buchanan and Thompson in 1886. A report discussing their observations was made during a survey in preparation for laying a transatlantic cable: ". . . the very remarkable undercurrent which is found setting in a southeasterly direction . . . almost on the Equator . . ." The current flows eastward, across the Atlantic Ocean beneath the Equator. It is 100 to 200 feet deep, moves at 3 knots and oscillates in a 200-mile band centered on the Equator. "It is characterized," Dr. Austin says, "by a remarkable increase in salinity when compared with surrounding waters." On the surface of the Atlantic, the Equatorial Current flows westward. In the Pacific, a similar undersea current, first reported in 1952, is the Cromwell Current. It also flows eastward, is at least 3,500 miles long and may be 8,000 miles long, and extends 125 miles on each side of the Equator. It moves at 2½ to 3 knots, and carries 40 million tons of water a minute. The Cromwell Current is named for the late Townsend Cromwell of the United States Fish and Wildlife Service, who made a careful study of it. A remarkable thing about the Cromwell Current is its shallowness. Only 65 to 1,640 feet beneath the Pacific, and 250 miles wide, it is 1,500 times as wide as it is deep. In 1959, another such undercurrent was first observed in the Indian Ocean.

More light on the squid. At 3,500 feet down in bathyscaphe *F.N.R.S. 3*, France's Cousteau and Houot watched a squid 1½ feet long in their searchlight's beams. It squirted white ink. They turned the light off. The ink glowed. Two squid nearby, as the men watched, shot out other luminescent clouds.

Aboard the vessel *Pillsbury*, a University of Miami research ship, Gilbert L. Voss reported, "We brought up five or six two-inch fire squids of a species new to science. I placed one of the tiny live animals under the microscope and slowly focused down upon it. To my amazement I found myself looking at a host of tiny glittering blue-green lights of almost ethereal beauty, like distant stars on a tropic night."

More squid are eaten by humans than any other sea creature except fish. They have the nearest thing to a well-developed brain among backboneless animals, and their greatest help to man may come not from providing him food but from the work now being done on their thick nerve fibers. The squid's system of nerve fibers constitutes, Dr. Voss says in the *National Geographic* for March, 1967, "the most massive inner signal system known in any animal." This nerve system, now being studied in laboratories, may help us understand our own nerves.

The deepest-dwelling animals. The Russians, including a

scientist named Belyaev, have been dredging in some of the deepest trenches in the bottom of the sea. As a result, Florida State's Bob Menzies tells me, they have almost doubled the number of animals known to live at the greatest depths, bringing the total known to 280. By today, these deepest dwellers include foraminifera (plankton), polychaete worms, isopods, amphipods, bivalves, and sea cucumbers. Dr. Torben Wolff of Denmark's *Galathea* expedition of the early 1950's, headed by Anton Bruun, not long ago reported to UNESCO on dredging the trenches. He said that there had been hauled up, from almost seven miles down, a perchlike fish, sea anemones, worms, and a shrimplike creature; these animals were caught by Russian, American, and Danish research vessels dredging in the trenches off Japan and the Philippines, and in the Kurile-Kamchatka Trench east of Siberia. "The reports of Wolff (1960) and Belyaev (1966) clearly demonstrate," says Bob Menzies, "that a sizable diverse fauna lives on the floor of the world trenches at depths greater than six thousand meters." Menzies thinks the animals of the greatest trenches are very similar to the animals of the ocean abyss. That is, the additional depth and greater pressure in the trenches do not cause the animals to be significantly different in morphology (size or shape) from those elsewhere on the abyssal bottom of the sea.

A principal characteristic of the deepest-dwelling animals, as reported in the recent past, has been that many of them are "giants of their species." This gigantism has been thought to be characteristic of animals in the great trenches. Bob Menzies, though, believes this is not so. He has found that size does not go up as the animals live deeper. One reason: He collects isopods, and he collects his biggest specimens from shallow water rather than the deepest parts of the trenches. Menzies himself did not haul up any gigantic specimens when he trawled the Milne-Edwards Deep off Peru. He also found that animals from shallow water in the Antarctic are larger than the deepest-dwelling animals.

Rose-colored mud may mean oil. Half to three-quarters of a mile beneath the surface, near some coasts, the bottom of the sea is the continental rise, the area between the continental slope and the abyssal plain of the ocean floor. The continental rise is present offshore, at the base of the continental slope, wherever there are no trenches. It is found off the coasts of the United States, Mozambique, Morocco, Kenya, India, Brazil, Argentina, and Angola.

How was the continental rise formed? Dr. Bruce C. Heezen found rose, rose-gray, and light rose-gray muds on the continental rise off Georgia and Florida. Dr. Heezen, Charles Hollister, and William Ruddiman, all of Columbia's Lamont Geological Observatory, concluded the muds were from the Triassic or Paleozoic red sediments of Nova Scotia, New Brunswick, and the Gulf of St. Lawrence. Dr. Heezen thinks a current, deep beneath the Atlantic, flowing parallel to the coast, transported the fine, rosy mud to the Georgia-Florida offshore area. These sediments built up over the past 200 million years, and so formed the continental rise. Dr. Heezen hauled up samples of the mud to analyze it. He photographed the bottom and found currents, ripples, and scour marks—clues to the underwater current. He found that deep-sea bottom currents off the East Coast of the United States along the continental rise do not flow in a northerly direction like the Gulf Stream, but instead flow in a southerly direction. With seismic investigations he found thick sediment beneath the upper continental rise and out toward the ocean floor. Most thick accumulations of marine sediments contain petroleum. No oil or gas wells ever have been drilled on the continental rise; all so far are on the much shallower (and nearer to shore) continental shelf. "While the continental rise is not exploited commercially at the present time," Dr. Heezen said, "the possibility of the ultimate retrieval of oil from the deep sea seems highly likely."

A cliff containing oil? Dr. Bruce Heezen, working aboard Duke University's oceanographic ship *Eastward*, brought up 100-million-year-old rocks from an escarpment of the Blake Plateau off Florida. "These," Dr. Heezen said in April, 1966, "are sedimentary rocks (the first found in these waters), and oil is found in sedimentary rock." The rock, perhaps an entire cliff of it, was found 10,000 to 12,500 feet down. Dr. Heezen also discovered strong ocean currents at these depths. It had previously been believed these were quiet waters.

The rocks he brought up were smooth and clean except for a black coating of manganese, and appeared to have been kept that way by currents that had washed away any sediment for perhaps millions of years.

With Robert D. (Sam) Gerard of Lamont as chief scientist, the JOIDES expedition (*J*oint *O*ceanographic *I*nstitution for *D*eep *E*arth *S*ampling—Columbia, Woods Hole, Scripps, and the Institute of Marine Science at the University of Miami) drilled six core holes in the continental shelf, slope, and Blake Plateau. One hole was drilled in 3,386 feet of water into 585 feet of sea bottom on the Blake Plateau. That was the record depth of water through which any hole was drilled until the Humble Oil & Refining Company, Houston, beat the record by drilling a hole in 4,777 feet of water. They found phosphate and, beneath the sea floor, fresh water which spouted up, through a drill string of pipes, 30 feet above the surface of the ocean.

On and around the Blake Plateau, Duke University scientists, including Dr. Orrin Pilkey, Dr. S. Duncan Heron, Dr. George Lintz, and John Newton, have taken more than 1,000 bottom samples and cores. Where the continental shelf gives way to the incline of the continental slope, they find the bottom sediment turns an eerie green. The green sediment contains large areas of glauconite sands. Glauconite is a green mineral that precipitates out of seawater and is a potential source of potash, another vital element in the manufacture of fertilizers.

Also found on the bottom along the North Carolina coast is sand, needed to replace eroding beaches; and black sands, or the so-called heavy mineral sands. Similar deposits of black sands elsewhere, the Duke University News Service points out, have been found to contain titanium, iron, chromium, gold, rare earths, and other elements.

"Only within the last decade," says Dr. Pilkey, "have serious efforts been made to develop large-scale ocean-mining methods. Already iron sands are being profitably exploited in shallow waters off Japan, as are tin sands off Ceylon and Indonesia, diamond-rich gravels off South Africa, and gold-bearing sands off Alaska. Our results should at least point out avenues for detailed exploration by any interested groups."

The United States Geological Survey has contracted with Duke University to begin a three-year search to pinpoint the minerals off North Carolina. Dr. Pilkey will sample the bottom of the sea from the continental margin to 1,500 miles offshore. Later, deep-diving submarines may go down to the bottom and look around. Dr. Henry L. Berryhill, Jr., of the Geological Survey will search for minerals at river mouths and under the sea close to shore.

Springtime in the abyss. Bob Menzies wants to know whether or not deep-sea isopods, tiny animals, reproduce on a regular schedule, or cycle. "The difficulty in sampling the sea floor at depths greater than 2,000 meters (over 6,000 feet)," he wrote in *Nature* of August 19, 1967, "is so great that even today there are not many samples." Among those few deep-sea samples there have been so few pregnant female isopods that Torben Wolff figured they were hiding in the mud in the bottom of the sea and so avoiding being captured by trawls. The seasons do not change in the deep sea, so far as we know, the way the seasons change on the surface where, as the water warms, plankton reproduce and multiply in the spring. However, in laboratories under constant conditions without the changing seasons, organisms have been found to breed according to the rhythms of the sea and the moon. From limited data—and limited isopods dredged up from the deep sea—Bob Menzies has strong evidence that the deepest isopods reproduce according to seasonal breeding cycles, just as do animals in shallow water where the seasons change greatly. In other words, men may not be able to tell when it's spring in the deepest, always cold, always dark, bottom of the sea. But the isopods have no difficulty whatever. They know.

Small fish clean bigger fish. We know they do because eye-witnesses beneath the sea and visitors to marine aquariums have seen it happen. Among the coral reefs off Florida, says the Miami Seaquarium's Captain Bill Gray, small fish enter the mouths of bigger ones, and clean the big ones' teeth. Some shrimp advertise, he says, that they are offering their cleaning services, by waving their antennae back and forth. The cleaners eat the material they collect and they are not gobbled up by the big fish. Besides cleaning teeth, the cleaners also clean diseased tissues, external surfaces, and gills of the big fish.

Captain Gray adds that the little creatures that he has observed cleaning and picking parasites from larger creatures are the neon gobies, butterfly fish, porkfish, and coral shrimp. The little porkfish—a resident of coral patches—is especially given to this form of food collection. The large fish that they have been seen helping in this fashion are principally the groupers, up to and including giant ones (to 500 pounds off Miami and the Florida Keys). Moray eels, Gray adds, also seem to welcome the services of cleaning fish.

The bottom of the sea rises to new heights. After the Good Friday, 1964, earthquake in and near Alaska, a U.S. Coast and Geodetic Survey oceanographer, Richard J. Malloy, pointed out the awesome strength of the quake. It was so strong that it caused the greatest uplift of land ever recorded. Between Kodiak and Montague Islands, in the Gulf of Alaska, the sea floor was raised by more than 50 feet. The area of the sea floor that was lifted up was approximately 500 by 125 miles.

The greatest rise of the bottom of the sea previously recorded followed the 1899 Yakutat Bay earthquake at Bancas Point, Disenchantment Bay, Alaska: $47\frac{1}{3}$ feet.

Other results of the quake: Islands were moved 15 to 20 feet closer together. Islands were raised as much as $31\frac{1}{2}$ feet. The bottom of the sea split open, leaving 50-foot-high cliffs on each side of the split. Another fracture was lengthened by 35 miles. In Seward, Alaska, the Upper Bay instantly became 90 to 120 feet deeper.

The Alaskan tremor, three geophysicists of the Coast Survey said, may have resulted from an "explosive force" in the earth 30 to 50 miles below sea level. This, they explained, may have been due to a sudden change in the structure or chemistry of the earth below Prince William Sound in the Gulf of Alaska. Here, 30 miles deep, the earth temperature is 2,200 degrees Fahrenheit, and rocks turn molten or plastic. When heated rock rises into upper layers, explosions may occur and the earth's crust may split open. Beneath the sea, the earth's crust becomes a thin, rigid layer. When something from inside the earth pushes it up, it fractures. Such tensions may have produced, the Coast Survey says, the many submarine trenches, seamounts, and faults in the crust on the bottom of the Pacific Ocean. Off Alaska, in the area where the earthquake occurred, the bottom of the sea is highly fractured, and the region is noted for earthquakes and volcanic activity.

Moving sand dunes on the bottom of the sea. Men who drill for oil on the ocean bed have discovered a new bottom hazard. Clay Hornick wrote in the Summer, 1967, *Petroleum Today*: "Equipment on the ocean bed has been covered by nomad-like sand dunes, some of them 30 feet in height, that endlessly move across the sea floor."

Another well-preserved object on the bottom of the sea. The bottom of the sea may turn out, as the discovery of the ancient galleon by *Aluminaut's* Art Markel suggests, to be a great preserver of objects, a "safe-deposit box." After Markel had seen the 500-year-old galleon off Spain, three men in the *Alvin* came upon an airplane the sea had preserved. They saw on the bottom off New England a World War II Navy F6F Bearcat, a fighter plane, apparently intact. It had gone down in 1944, when Navy pilots were flying F6F's off New England. "*Alvin*," John Schilling writes, "was completing dive 209 a few miles west of Hydrographer's Canyon on the continental slope at a depth of 5,214 feet. In the sub were the pilot, Marvin McCamis; co-pilot, Edward Bland; and scientist, Barrie Dale." The men were obtaining sediment samples (containing plankton) and taking pictures a few feet above the continental slope. The dive took place on August 13, 1967. "The dive was three-and-one-half hours old," Mr. Schilling says, "when Mr. Dale noticed an object out of the port window which resembled an aircraft. The object was just out of the range of lights. His first thoughts were, 'I've been down here too long and my eyes are not focusing properly.' Mr. Dale reported to pilot McCamis what he saw and the sub turned around in order that the lights could be used to identify the unknown object. There in the illumination of the lights was a complete World War II F6F just as if it had landed after a mission. It was sitting upright, its wheels retracted, its canopy open, and its instruments apparently intact. Its pilot probably left the plane in the air or on the surface. The plane, submerged for 23 years, showed no signs of marine fouling or deterioration."

Engineers of the Bendix Corporation, the June-July 1968, *American Oceanography* reported, have come up with reasons to explain why the depths of the sea may preserve objects, as they preserved the F6F and a galleon from Columbus' day. The top 500 feet of the ocean are hazardous—that is, there are such things as fouling, dangerous marine life, temperature changes, strong currents, and so forth, and all of them harmful to equipment. But below 500 feet, Bendix reports, electronic packages last seven times as long as they do on land. The company figures this is due to even temperature, slow or no currents, and little turbulence.

Dust storm beneath the sea. Bob Hill dived in *Star II* in the Gulf of Mexico off Louisiana: "The top fifty feet of the Gulf here," he told me, "is like a mud bath. The bottom of the Gulf is worse. Here the Mississippi dumps its silt—a cloud, an undersea dust storm on the bottom. You can go from forty feet visibility to two feet or even inches as you enter the cloud. Cruising over this dust storm is like flying over a cloud. Diving into it in *Star II* is like flying into one."

But of all the discoveries on the bottom of the sea, nothing is quite as exciting to anyone as to see with his own eyes what is there.

Some 1,500 feet beneath the surface, near the Bahamas, Hill cruised in *Star II*. He slowly passed a steep and spectacular

Asherah has been one of the most successful of the early deep-diving submarines. Men aboard her have found ancient sunken ships, valuable red coral for jewelry, skipjack tuna, and huge Hawaiian spiny lobsters.

Deep Diver can take down a diver and let him out on the bottom. She has done so as deep as 700 feet. At 700 feet, Roger Cook and Denny Breese stepped out, worked fifteen minutes—deepest working dive.

Artist's conception shows the first of six deep submergence rescue vehicles (DSRV's) planned by U.S. Navy. DSRV is shown mating to guide wires aboard mother nuclear sub that carries her piggyback.

Drawing shows Trieste II. The bathyscaphe is assigned to Submarine Flotilla One, in Pacific. Bathyscaphes are only craft capable of going farther down than deep-diving submarines.

First men in history stand atop the summit of a mountain beneath the sea, Seahorse Shoal, South China Sea. ESSA Ensign Paul Larsen (left) and Harris B. Stewart hold a large holothurian (sea cucumber).

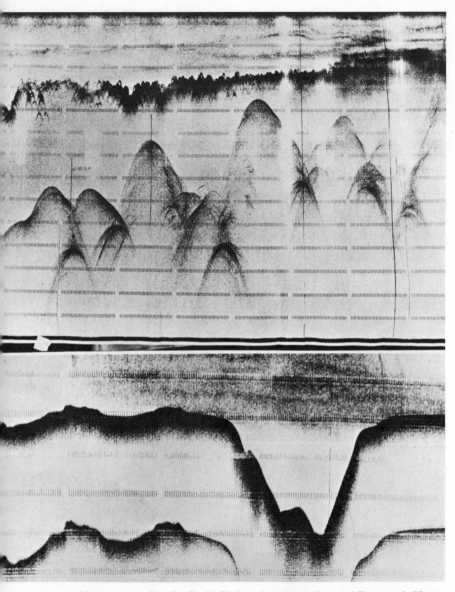

Shoran recording by Duke University research vessel Eastward. *Upper dark layer is ocean surface. Second dark layer is deep scattering layer. Bottom graph, Hatteras submarine canyon.*

Seascape is a coral niche on Seahorse Shoal. Scene is 40 feet beneath the surface, 90 miles west of Borneo. The "bird bath" in the picture is a colony, or apartment house, of hundreds of white corals.

This 15-foot-long sea serpent is probably a colony of small organisms. Picture of serpent was made by Mobot, a robot that works on undersea oil wells, and was built by Hughes Aircraft for Shell Oil.

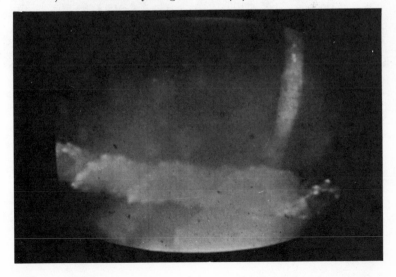

Scuba divers from Miami (Florida) Seaquarium discovered the jawfish. They were 60 feet down beneath the Gulf Stream. Pearl-colored, 4-inch-long fish build a tunnel in bottom. They dart into tunnel tail first.

Gorgonia grows on luxuriant coral reefs around Great Swan Island, a little-known U.S. possession in the Caribbean Sea. Photographed during the 1960 oceanographic expedition of the USCGS Explorer.

Porkfish (Anistremus virginicus) *nose around the coraline sand bottom near Swan Island. Date: 1960. "Taken by me," Harris Stewart writes, "at a depth of about 20 feet with natural light in the reefs."*

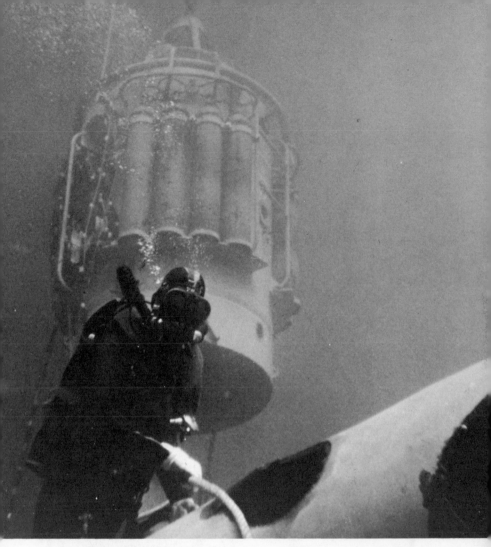

Divers Glen Taylor and Arthur Pachette in 1967 went down 636 feet in an Ocean Systems pressure chamber, got out, and worked there. "Finally," says the Southwest Research Institute, "science is beginning to catch up with Jules Verne beneath the sea just as it has tried to catch up with him in space."

Eighty miles SSW of Nantucket, Massachusetts, the USCGS Explorer took photo 260 fathoms down. The flower-like animals are deep-sea anemones. Mounds and tracks of other bottom-dwellers are shown.

Plankton—tiny animal and plant life of the ocean—as it looked to crew members of Alvin and was sketched by them. Through Star II's viewport, the author saw the sea teeming with the pinpoint-sized plankton.

undersea cliff. He saw limestone caves in it, and he saw mountains around it. Landing on a plateau, he switched on his floodlights, and gazed out through the viewports. He saw a light, muddy sediment where there lived vast numbers of 3-inch shrimp.

At 2,000 feet down, as far down as *Star II* can go, Hill switched off his lights. He was goggle-eyed as he saw the fish of the deep sea—some had long rows of light organs along their sides. He saw shrimp—some of them glowed. Both fish and shrimp put on for Hill a spectacular display of luminescence.

"The bioluminescence in the fish—the different lights, red, greens—I saw them as they flashed past the viewports, the different colors going by. It was beautiful. It was great. It was like watching stars go by on a night flight in an airplane."

The Case of the Sunken H-Bomb

21

The thing was shaped like a torpedo. At its stern it had something a torpedo does not have: a tail like a box kite. Like a torpedo, it was making its way through the sea. But it was far deeper than any torpedo; it was half a mile beneath the surface. It was traveling only 20 to 30 feet above the sea floor that half a mile down. Again unlike a torpedo, it was traveling at the end of a cable—at the end of 5,600 feet of cable that ran up to a ship on the surface.

The thing was a robot that had journeyed to the bottom of the sea to look for something. It was what is called side-looking sonar. It is also called Ocean Bottom Search Sonar.

It was looking for a lost H-bomb in the Mediterranean Sea, off the coast of Spain, offshore from the small town of fishermen and tomato farmers that is known as Palomares.

The H-bomb had fallen in a crash in January, 1966, of two United States Air Force planes: a B-52 jet bomber (which carried the bomb) and a KC-135 tanker (refueling the bomber with several thousand gallons of largely-kerosene jet fuel). One of the B-52's engines caught fire and the bomber exploded, damaging the KC-135. Both planes plunged to earth. Seven airmen died. The accident took place almost six miles above Spain. Four H-bombs, none of them armed and none of them about to explode, fell from the B-52. Three were found on land. The fourth was believed to have fallen into the Mediterranean.

Could it be found?

The missing H-bomb was about 12 feet long and 2 feet thick. It was like looking for a needle in a thousand haystacks.

The search could not even have been attempted without the latest equipment—including new deep-diving submarines and side-looking sonar.

To start the search a fleet assembled off the coast near Palomares. Coming largely from the United States Sixth (Mediterranean) Fleet, it was called Task Force 65. It included 25 Navy ships and 3,000 naval officers and men and a whole armada of deep-diving submarines—the only time so many have worked together. Task Force 65 was commanded by Rear Admiral William S. Guest, 52, who said: "I would prefer combat to this any time." Admiral Guest knew whereof he spoke. In World War II he was credited with being the first aviator to sink a Japanese ship.

In Washington, D.C., a group headed by Rear Admiral L. V. Swanson supervised and supported Task Force 65. "By all counts," says a Navy report, "the operation . . . was the largest concentrated underwater search in history, exceeding the numbers of persons involved, problems overcome and logistic requirements of even the remarkable and successful search for the lost submarine *Thresher* three years previous."

The United States not only had to find the H-bomb somewhere on the bottom of the Mediterranean; it also had to pick it up off the bottom and bring it home. There were two principal reasons: (1) The H-bomb could not be left where people might even think it was a danger. It was not going to explode, but there was no way people could know that. Neither was it going to give off lethal radiation. And (2) the H-bomb had to be recovered by the United States to prevent the remote possibility that an enemy power might come along and get it.

Task Force 65 took up its position offshore where a trail of debris, mostly airplane and bomb bits and pieces, led from the scene of the crash into the Mediterranean.

The Naval Oceanographic Office made charts on the site and evaluated tides, the bottom, and deep currents (for the submarines).

The Navy sought and obtained help from American companies in its search. Supervising the entire job was Ocean Systems, Incorporated, a company specializing in diving and sea-bottom work. Ocean Systems, an affiliate of Union Carbide Corporation and General Precision Equipment Corporation, numbers among its people Rear Admiral E. C. Stephan, United States Navy (Ret.), a former oceanographer of the Navy; Chet Smith; Captain Ray M. Pitts, United States Navy (Ret.), who was the company's representative with Task Force 65; and Jon Lindbergh, the deep-sea diver. Ocean Systems used 11 other companies as subcontractors to help, and it rounded up the biggest fleet of deep-diving submarines ever assembled. In the murky waters off the Spanish coast, men made more voyages to the bottom of the sea in less than three months—February-April 1966—than they ever have made in any other place or in such a short time. Their voyages off Spain were more urgent, too. To Admiral Guest there was no "maybe" about what had to be done: "We have to take the weapon," he said.

The H-bomb was recovered, but it took a lot of doing.

For the underseas fleet to make the search for the nuclear weapon, Ocean Systems obtained a Cubmarine, the *PC3B*, from John H. Perry's Cubmarine Company, in Palm Beach, Florida. Though small—she weighs only 550 pounds—the *PC3B* is a true submarine and operates just like the Navy's submarines—that is, she takes on water ballast, and, using her bow planes and main propulsion motors, she dives rather than sinks to the bottom. Jon Lindbergh was one of the people who rode in her into the waters offshore of Palomares. The Cubmarine was flown out of the Palm Beach, Florida, International Airport on the night of February 11, 1966, in an Air Force C-141, a transport plane. With her were senior crew member James D. Casey of Lantana, Florida; Jim Jolley of Delray Beach, Florida; and Chief Pilot Mike Adams of West Palm Beach.

The Cubmarine, in 59 dives, spent a total of 126 hours underwater. She found lots of airplane wreckage between 150 and 200 feet down on the sea floor, Mike Adams said later; she helped follow the trail to sea. She ran into and bounced off rock outcroppings on the bottom. The 22-foot-long Cubmarine also had rough going in 8-foot-high surface waves.

From the Naval Ordnance Test Station (today the Naval Weapons Center), China Lake, California, Willis Forman arrived with the Navy's *Deep Jeep*, an acorn-shaped, two-man, deep-diving vessel. She had been inoperable for nine months prior to the request of the Chief of Naval Operations for all available deep submergence vehicles to assist in the H-bomb search. Nevertheless, she and her crew were airborne en route to Spain within 30 hours. Off Spain men aboard her made dives as deep as 1,900 feet and averaged four hours under water each dive.

The torpedo-shaped side-looking sonar arrived off Palomares after a long haul:

At midnight, January 21, 1966, four days after the collision, a phone rang in Baltimore at the Underseas Division of the Westinghouse Defense and Space Center. The gist of the call, which came through the Air Force Strategic Air Command at Omaha, Nebraska: "Can we have your side-looking sonar for the search off Spain?"

The only sonar unit available had just been flown to Texas for exploration for oil offshore.

Said the Western Geophysical Corporation in Texas: "You can have it back immediately."

And back it came, from Texas via the Barksdale Air Force Base, Louisiana, to Andrews Air Force Base, Maryland. And from there it was flown to Spain.

Westinghouse engineers went to Spain on another plane. They changed planes three times, took a four-hour drive over Spanish roads, and then took a whaleboat trip to reach Navy ships offshore. They had left Baltimore on Monday, January 24. On Wednesday they started looking for the H-bomb.

The minesweepers *Pinnacle, Rival, Salute,* and *Notable* in turn pulled the side-looking sonar back and forth, back and forth, crossing and crisscrossing a 45-square-mile patch of the Mediterranean.

The side-looking sonar is unique. It is 12 feet long and 1,500 pounds in weight. It is towed 200 to 400 feet above the bottom. It scans the ocean floor with a beam of high-frequency sound. The echoes come back and are converted into electrical signals that go up the long cable to the ship towing the sonar and turn into scan lines on 400-foot-long rolls of paper. The scan lines are rough pictures of what the sonar has found—pictures of hills, plains, valleys, and objects on the bottom.

This sonar was fully designed as recently as 1965. The need for it was shown when, in 1963, the U.S.S. *Thresher* went down. Once constructed, the side-looking sonar first proved its worth by finding the main fuselage of a jet plane that had crashed in Lake Michigan, killing 30 persons. It also had spotted some wrecked offshore oil platforms in the Gulf of Mexico in 1966. It also recently has found ocean-floor faults caused by earthquakes in the seabed off Alaska.

Two additional side-looking sonars were built in a hurry by Westinghouse's Parker Road Plant in Baltimore and sent to Spain.

One of them crashed into a minesweeper and had to be repaired. Another hit a jagged submarine cliff which snapped the line and sent it to the bottom. Men in the Cubmarine found it—and it became after the H-bomb itself the second most valuable object recovered off Spain.

Altogether, three sonars spotted over 260 items on the bottom, including metal shavings, a filing cabinet, boulders, an ancient anchor, and old Spanish cannon. Most of the items located, however, were from the wreckage of the two planes.

Six good contacts—any one of which might have been the H-bomb—were found by the sonar on the sea floor. They were near a point six miles offshore where a Palomares fisherman, Francisco Simo-Orts, said he had seen the bomb fall.

The next problem was to direct a deep-diving submarine to the spot. The submarine, flown over, was the *Alvin*, piloted by Bill Rainnie, Marvin McCamis, and Valentine Wilson. The pilots worked two men at a time aboard her. Dr. Earl E. Hays headed 11 Woods Hole men who also went to Spain.

The *Alvin*—her nickname is the Chipmunk—on a sunny morning was launched into the water from her acting mother ship, the LSD (*Landing Ship Dock*) *Fort Snelling*. A minesweeper tried to talk her down via underwater telephone— much as an airport control tower talks an airplane down in a thick fog—right to somewhere near a sonar contact that the Navy called Object 261.

"This is complex," said Melvin Hiller, head of Westinghouse's Underseas Division's oceanographic instrumentation section. "Even if the sonar spotted something, we could never tell precisely where on the ocean floor that was. We had to know how fast the minesweeper was pulling the sonar. We had no map of the ocean floor. We had little information on ocean currents. Basically, we could never tell exactly the relationship of the sonar and the ship."

Underwater navigation and communications were two of the most serious and most frustrating problems off Spain, John L. Barringer, Jr., manager of submarine operations of Ocean Systems, said later. The Cubmarine has since worked on undersea navigation and communications for the Office of Naval Research and the Naval Oceanographic Office. "Results," said Barringer, in *Geo Marine Technology*, "look very promising." Simple transmitters and receivers similar, he says, to those apparently used by sea creatures in communicating with each other, have been transmitting messages from water to air—"which may open the door to a whole new system of sub-surface to surface communications."

The *Alvin* descended and neared the bottom, about half a mile down. She was buffeted about by previously unknown currents that varied in both speed and direction.

There is very little in the way of a shallow continental shelf off the Mediterranean coast of Spain. Through their port-holes, the *Alvin's* men peered out instead at undersea moun-tainsides similar to those in nearby Spain. Granite blocks pro-truded from the mountains. A crash could have been fatal. There would be rough water on the surface later. Once the *Alvin's* crew had to ride out a surface storm. The sea was too rough for the submarine and her men to be picked up by the *Fort Snelling*.

With the sub's floodlights on, the Chipmunk's men could see about 30 feet. Without them they could not see at all. Said *Ocean Science News:* "We hope they come through without fatal mishap." *Ocean Science News*, one of the publications that knows the oceans best, was aware of the danger involved.

On their tenth dive the men aboard the *Alvin*—piloted on this trip by McCamis and Wilson—around 2,500 feet down, found a scar, or groove, on the side of an undersea mountain. Such a mark might have been made by an H-bomb moving down the slope.

Later, over the furrow again, the *Alvin* backed her way down the slope. She backed to keep the furrow in view through her bow ports and to keep her propeller clear of the sloping bottom.

The scar took her to a strange-looking thing on the steep 70-degree mountain slope: Object 261. With their floodlights on, the crew decided it looked like a parachute—the parachute attached to an H-bomb that slows down its descent and lets the bombing plane that dropped it get away before the explosion. The men also could see a cylindrical silhouette of what they thought was the bomb. They took photographs at 2,532 feet down. The resulting pictures looked like the bomb. It turned out that Object 261 was the bomb. It was found on March 15, or about two months after it dropped. Until that date the Navy had expected, its report says, "that the most probable outcome was considered to be failure to locate the weapon." "It was," said *Ocean Science News* for May 12, 1966, "eyeball detection and tracking (in the old American Indian sense) that first found the bomb."

The *Alvin's* dive that found the bomb lasted 11 hours. Now came the job of bringing the bomb to the surface. Said the late Jack Long, then editor of *Ocean Science News*, "If the bomb is recovered this will be even more remarkable than its identification." No lost object ever had been found and brought up from half a mile down beneath the ocean's surface.

The *Mizar*, a Navy oceanographic ship that had taken part in the search for the *Thresher*, parked right over the bomb site. To help keep a guard over the bomb on the bottom, *Aluminaut* stood watch-and-watch with *Alvin*. That is, one of them stood still or hovered right beside the H-bomb all the time lest it slide away into a crevasse and get lost. *Aluminaut*, managed by Art Markel and captained by Bob Serfass, baby-sat with the bomb for 22 hours at one stretch. When *Aluminaut* for the first time approached the *Alvin* at the site of the bomb, their pilots talked to each other by voice. The meetings of the *Alvin* and *Aluminaut* at the H-bomb location were the first rendezvous of submarines at any such depth as half a mile down. There were three meetings between the *Alvin* and *Aluminaut*. They took place, says Reynolds International, the *Aluminaut's* operators, "in a vast world of complete darkness. The two submarines could make out each other's external lights at distances of 200 yards, but otherwise visibility with their own lights was limited to about 20 feet. High-resolution sonars on the two vessels were used as homing devices during the closure operations."

Aluminaut's original crew during the H-bomb hunt consisted of Bob Serfass, captain; Bob Canary, assistant captain; Dennison Breese, electronics technician; and Harold A. Little. L. C. Morris, Reynolds Sub-Marine's operation manager, also worked aboard. Crew members added later were William J. McDevitt, Edwin C. Quinn, Jr., and John F. Lowell. Jim Cooney was electrical technician.

"You never know in this business where you're going to be from one day to the next," Cooney had said to me. "I was on the H-bomb, over in Spain. The hunt was an experience.

"On the bottom off Spain," he recalled, "we were exploring low foothills. The *Aluminaut* picked up about five thousand pounds of mud scraping the hillsides. Even after we dropped all our normal ballast of shotgun pellets, we were still heavy. We should have been rising. We were not. I broke out in a cold sweat of puzzlement—not much fear.

"We tried to run along the bottom, our two diving planes up, like a plane taking off. We left the bottom that way.

"On the surface, the sea washed away that extra two and one-half tons of muck. It made the sea look milky."

With her mechanical arm the *Alvin* managed to fasten a 3-inch-in-circumference polypropylene line to the bomb, running down from the *Mizar* on the surface. The *Alvin, Naval Research Reviews* explains, did this job by grasping the parachute in her claw and pulling the chute out on the undersea mountainside. Then she took a grappling hook in her claw and entangled it among the parachute shroud lines. This had to be done carefully to avoid tangling the arm itself in the lines. "It was the first time," *Naval Research Reviews* says, "such a task had been performed by a submersible." As the bomb was hauled upward, the line snapped. The bomb slipped away. It vanished. Said one official, "We misplaced it."

The *Alvin* after many more dives (she made 34 altogether in search of the H-bomb and spent 228 hours under water) and after nine agonizing days found it again. The *Alvin's* men, this time Rainnie and McCamis, spotted it by first seeing a furrow and then the parachute. The bomb had not gone into the crevasse. But it was deeper now: 2,850 feet down. The mountain slope was gentler here: only 35 degrees.

The *Alvin* marked the site of the bomb with a flashing light and pingers to emit sound and thus make it easier to return to the bomb.

Another underwater robot now came into action. The first one, the Westinghouse side-looking sonar, either had located the bomb or at least had pointed out a very likely site for the *Alvin* to explore, and the bomb had proved to be there. The second robot would bring the bomb to the surface.

Richard Heller of the Naval Ordnance Test Station, Pasadena, California, told me how the job was done. The robot was CURV (for *C*able-controlled *U*nderwater *R*ecovery *Ve*hicle). CURV had been recovering research torpedoes off California at depths of up to 2,000 feet. (The Navy plans to give CURV a capacity to operate 7,000 feet down.) CURV is run from a surface ship by cable controls by Howard Talkington, Herman (Bud) Kunz, and Joe Barkich. They watch a TV screen to see what is happening to CURV on the bottom. Her TV cameras, with RCA tubes like those that have photographed the moon, showed the men upstairs (on the surface ship, in this case the *Petrel*, a submarine rescue vessel) what went on as, with her mechanical arm, CURV tried to pick up the H-bomb.

CURV at first couldn't manage it. New tools had to be made on the spot—on the ocean, over the H-bomb, that is. As this was the first time that any such task ever had been attempted, this was hardly surprising. Robert Pace of the Naval Ordnance Test Station, aboard the U.S.S. *Cascade*, designed a four-point grappling hook, or grapnel. A nylon line was attached to it. CURV went down, maneuvered by the TV-watchers on the *Petrel,* and shoved the grapnel into the shrouds of the parachute. The prongs of the grapnel entangled some of them. In addition, on each of the four prongs, there was a spring-loaded bar that snapped shut into place behind the parachute shrouds so that they could not possibly slip off the prongs.

Now came one of the tensest moments of the entire search and recovery of the H-bomb.

After CURV had shoved the grapnel into the parachute shrouds, CURV took a strain on the line and on the shrouds. Then Wilson and McCamis in the *Alvin* went down to have a look. They were to make sure that the bomb was still attached to the parachute and had not separated.

"The strain on the line and parachute shrouds had stirred up the bottom silt considerably," *Naval Research Reviews* reports, "reducing visibility from about 25 or 30 feet, to which the pilots had been accustomed at that depth, to about zero. Cautiously, they edged into the cloud of silt, peering intently into the reflected glare of the spotlight beam. Suddenly, immediately in front of them, they confronted the parachute, part of which billowed above the ocean floor like a circus tent and part of which, apparently, had rolled up around the bomb, encasing it like a mummy."

If the *Alvin* became tangled in the chute, the men knew, they probably would be unable to free themselves, and probably would be enshrouded for good.

On the surface, almost 3,000 feet above them, Admiral Guest knew the same thing. "There was almost a disaster. We had no way of bringing them up," he said.

Val Wilson, piloting, made a sharp right turn and slid the *Alvin* out from under the chute. It had been a near thing.

CURV came back down to the chute with a second grapnel and drove it home into the shrouds. There were now two four-pronged hooks rammed into the lines of the chute. There were two nylon lines running from the hooks to the surface. CURV tried to put a third grapnel into place and almost got tangled in the parachute, so gave up the attempt. It had taken CURV three days to get the two grapnels in place. The H-bomb now was hauled upward on the two lines. It took one hour to hoist the bomb safely to the surface.

As the bomb approached the surface, Navy frogmen (scuba divers) went down and attached additional lines. At 8:45 A.M. on April 7, 1966, the bomb was deposited on the *Petrel's* deck.

The men who had originally gone over to Palomares, Spain, with the Westinghouse side-looking sonar had been told they would be there—along with all the other searchers—for two weeks. They stayed 76 days. Though their sonar may have located the bomb, the Westinghouse engineers themselves never saw it. "I was on the flagship *Albany*," said Morris A. Ransone. "As we passed the *Petrel*, all we could see was the shroud on the *Petrel's* deck. Beneath it was the bomb." (Besides Ransone and Melvin Hiller, other Westinghouse side-looking sonar team members included Istvan B. Gereben, Joseph Laing, Ted A. Turner, Louis F. Meyers, Barnie A. Parker, William Reave, Fred Brimberg, Robert S. Jones, Robert M. Silvis, Tom W. Brogan, Neil C. Miller, Robert R. Natale, Henry M. Gruen, Carl J. Modlin, Robert Underwood, Robert L. Gollwitzer, William F. Grauch, Donald F. Heinlein, Gerald J. Schoffs, William D. Shisler, Raymond C. Fischer, and Otis W. Lovell. The youngest team member was Rockne F. Cooke, 18 years old.)

Aboard the *Petrel*, the bomb itself, said Christopher Morris of the *London Express* News Service, was "shaped like the silver foil container for a good quality Havana cigar. There were even a few barnacles stuck to the bomb. Its gray parachute lay alongside and the yellow cradle to which it was attached was still fixed to the center of the bomb." The occasion was the first time the United States ever had displayed a modern nuclear weapon. It had to be displayed so the world would know the United States had managed to recover it. The bomb had dents in it. "Of course it is dented," Admiral Guest said. "It fell thirty thousand feet and hit the sea bottom twice."

To celebrate the bomb's recovery, Task Force 65 sailed past Palomares at night with lights blazing. And the Cubmarine's Mike Adams and other successful bomb-hunters put on black berets.

The seas contain many things that over the centuries have been "lost beyond recovery." As much as one-fifth of the gold and silver men have produced is lost in sunken treasure ships, and these precious metals are soaring in value. More valuable are ships sunk during both world wars, and their cargoes. Some of the items lost in the sea may now be recovered because the H-bomb hunt has shown how to do it. Deep-diver Jon Lindbergh has announced he'll scout the sunken Italian luxury liner *Andrea Doria* off Nantucket. She's believed to hold over $5 million in currency, jewels, and gold.

Curiously enough, the search by eyewitnesses for the H-bomb, at about a half mile down, took place at just about the same depth where, in 1934, William Beebe and Otis Barton in a bathysphere had become the first eyewitnesses in all human history of the depths of the sea. Thus, history repeated itself: Americans had twice done something significant at half a mile down.

There was no precedent for the search and recovery of the bomb. At the time the nuclear submarine *Thresher* sank in April, 1963, the *Alvin* and *Aluminaut* were not even in existence. Neither was the side-looking sonar. Not since Russia's Sputnik first orbited the earth in 1957 to become the first man-made satellite had there been such a step forward by any science, in this case oceanography. The search and recovery of the H-bomb was that rarest of events in the annals of the human race: something new under the sun.

The Submarines for Four Miles Down

22

The United States Navy is beginning to build the deepest-diving submarines in history. They will carry men to depths of 20,000 feet (almost four miles). Only one other planned submarine, the Westinghouse *Deepstar 20,000*, will be able to dive that deep.

The first submarine under the Navy program, the Deep Submergence Systems Project, as it is called, will be a rescue submarine.

The first rescue sub, *DSRV-1* (*D*eep *S*ubmergence *R*escue *V*ehicle number 1), now being constructed, will join the fleet before 1970.

DSRV-1 will not have the capacity to dive 20,000 feet. She will go to a minimum of 3,500 feet and will not collapse short of a depth of 5,250 feet. Later rescue submarines will go deeper.

As a rescue submarine, *DSRV-1* will have the ability to do something not possible today: She will be able to take men off a disabled submarine in deep water. She could, if necessary, go to the rescue of the crew on a nuclear submarine trapped beneath the Arctic ice.

There will be three men in the crew of *DSRV-1:* pilot, co-pilot, and a hospital corpsman. They will be able to bring off officers and crew, 24 survivors a trip, from a disabled submarine on the bottom as far as two-thirds of a mile down.

Speed is vital in the case of a submarine in distress. Eventually, the Navy plans, its rescue submarines will be able to be flown to any disabled submarine anywhere in the world within 24 hours, and to have the last men off the troubled craft within 50 hours.

One hundred years ago Jules Verne anticipated the way the DSRV's will function. He wrote that the *Nautilus* had a boat that a man could enter, through a double hatch, underwater. The double hatch consisted of a hatch in the *Nautilus* and one in the boat. With both hatches tightly shut, the man then detached the small boat from the *Nautilus* and so left the submarine and rose to the surface. Similarly, the DSRV will attach herself to the hatch of a sunken sub to remove survivors.

The Navy has worked out a carefully detailed plan for the operation of DSRV's—a world-wide rescue service. Should there be a disaster to a United States submarine a few years from now, the rescue service would instantly start moving.

When the report of a submarine in trouble is received, a DSRV will be flown to the nearest port equipped with a suitable airfield. The DSRV will travel aboard Lockheed's C-141, or Starlifter, or aboard the still later, bigger Lockheed C-5A, the biggest cargo plane ever built. The Wright brothers' original flight of the first airplane, in 1903, was 105 feet long. The cargo compartment alone of the C-5A is 145 feet long.

A second plane will carry to the most suitable port near the disaster a support van that contains all necessary handling and rescue equipment for the rescue submarine.

At the same time the two planes are heading for the rescue port, a Navy nuclear submarine will be approaching the same port at full speed.

The DSRV, after being unloaded from the airplane, will be attached "piggyback" to the nuclear submarine which will take her to the sunken sub.

Radio buoys released by the distressed submarine, the Navy says, will guide the rescuers to the scene of the accident.

Once close to the wreck, the rescue sub will detach herself from the mother nuclear sub. Diving to the disabled craft, she will home in on her by sonar at a speed of 3 to 5 knots. When she is close enough, the DSRV will use underwater TV, floodlights, and high resolution sonar to travel the last few yards.

Using a mechanical arm, the rescue sub will clear away any debris over the hatch of the sunken submarine and will cut the cable running to the messenger radio buoy that beckoned her to the sunken submarine.

The DSRV next will join a hatch on her bottom to a hatch on the sunken sub.

This will take some doing. Undersea currents, pressure, and darkness complicate the problem. So does the possibility that the sunken submarine may be lying at an angle.

The DSRV will attempt to latch on exactly to the other sub's hatch with the help of a small computer that will allow for pitching, yawing, currents, surging, heaving, and swaying. The computer and a mercury trim-and-list system will control rolling.

Two thrusters, forward and aft, in the DSRV will enable her to push herself sideways and so get into the right position over the hatch. The thrusters are propellers that push sideways, located in tunnels that run from one side of the sub to the other.

"By use of these thrusters in various combinations," Lieutenant Commander Wes Larson of the Deep Submergence Systems Project explains, "the vehicle will be controlled in the yaw and pitch axes, or the DSRV can be kept on an even keel, yet bodily moved up and down or from side to side at a speed of one knot." Similar thrusters have been put on a few modern merchant ships for pushing them sideways as they dock or leave the pier.

Once the DSRV has joined her hatch to that of the sunken sub, the DSRV then pumps the escape skirt dry, equalizes the pressure between herself and the distressed submarine so that the hatches can be opened, and proceeds to rescue the crew of the sunken sub. Into her, the DSRV also can pass oxygen and lithium hydroxide to keep the air breathable and so lengthen the time of survival of men in the wreck.

The DSRV then travels, 100 feet a minute either upward or downward, to the mother nuclear sub that brought her. She bolts onto a hatch of the mother sub, and into her she releases the survivors of the sunken craft. She goes back to the wreck for more survivors.

Everything the DSRV does in making a rescue, according to today's plans, she can do beneath the sea. She does not even have to surface to discharge the people she rescues.

DSRV-1 will be 49 feet long, 8 feet in beam, 30 tons in weight. She will have an inner hull of three spheres or balls, 7½ feet in diameter, made of strong high yield (HY-140) steel —or titanium. As in the case of *Deep Quest*, the three spheres will be interconnected and men may step from one sphere to another.

DSRV-1 will be battery-powered. A propeller at her stern will drive her forward or backward. It will be in a shroud—a circular metal protection.

Harold Bernstein of Deep Submergence points out how great an improvement in submarine rescue the DSRV will represent. The McCann rescue bell, which can go only 850 feet down, he says, "is the Navy's current submarine rescue device. The McCann bell is lowered from a special surface ship (which immediately limits its availability and prevents it from operating under the ice), has no search ability (which means the exact location of the disabled submarine must be known to the surface ship), and the bell can carry only seven passengers on each trip to the surface." High seas can also be a limiting factor.

The prime contractor for the Deep Submergence Systems Project for management and engineering support is Northrop's Nortronics Division. The Lockheed Missiles and Space Company is building the DSRV. The Deep Submergence Systems Project is directed by Captain William M. Nicolson, first in his class at the Naval Academy in 1941, and an engineering-duty officer who has served aboard the carrier *Philippine Sea* and the cruiser *Oregon City*.

The Navy normally goes a long time between submarine disasters. It lost the *Scorpion* in 1968. It lost the *Thresher* in 1963, and the Deep Submergence Systems Project was a result of that. Twenty-four years earlier, in 1939, the *Squalus* went down. The *S-51* and *S-4* were lost in the 1920's. The United States' first major submarine disaster was that of the *F-4* off Honolulu in 1915.

Eventually there will be six Navy rescue submarines located at widely-spaced strategic harbors around the world. That will enable them to get fast to the scene of any submarine disaster. In the years between submarine disasters, the rescue subs are expected to do a good deal of exploring the bottom of the sea on their own. Says the Navy, "The DSRV may be used for oceanographic research when not required for rescue missions. Scientists, technicians, and divers could be transported in the DSRV to perform secondary missions, including sonar research, bottom coring, aiding man-in-the-sea experiments, mapping, scientific viewing, and temperature current measurements."

Besides 20,000-foot-deep rescue submarines, the Navy is also planning 20,000-foot-deep search submarines. These craft will be able to search the deep-sea floor for lost objects, as the Cubmarines *Alvin* and *Aluminaut* can do. The Navy also plans 20,000-foot-deep submarines that can recover objects from the sea floor, as CURV did with the H-bomb.

United States naval officers for deep-diving submarines have started training.

With Submarine Development Group One in the Pacific, aboard the bathyscaphe *Trieste II*, a new kind of naval officer —the hydronaut—is being trained to command and navigate the new deep-diving submarines.

Future hydronauts first spend several weeks working at a mockup on dry land of the *Trieste II* control sphere in San Diego, California. Later they must make approximately six successful dives as one of the three men in the cramped capsule of *Trieste II*. It's a tighter squeeze than aboard any spaceship. *Trieste II* carries a pilot, copilot, and observer. The prospective hydronaut, says Lieutenant Commander E. E. Henifin, officer in charge of *Trieste II*, can take any of these three positions.

Besides furthering oceanographic research with its future 20,000-footers, the Navy already supports oceanography in all kinds of ways: at its own establishments, such as the Office of Naval Research (ONR), in universities, in oceanographic institutions, and in private companies. This is logical. Oceanography has been defined as "the study of the seas and all that in them is." Everything that pertains to the sea is important to national defense, and therefore is of interest to the Navy.

The 20,000-foot-deep submarines, says Samuel Feldman, "will permit the development of a new generation of deep-sea craft and provide the means for exploring the heretofore nonreachable ocean depths."

The Dropoff into the Deep

23

What is it like to prowl the continental slope? Two men in *Deep Jeep* saw for themselves.

The continental slope is a great hillside beneath the sea. It starts at the seaward edge of the continental shelf. The slope—the hillside—slants downward to the abyss of the ocean, the deep-sea floor.

From the shoreline out to where the continental slope begins, the ocean is shallow: 400 or 600 feet deep, rarely over 1,000 feet deep. Once the continental slope is reached, the sea floor plunges downward, till the ocean is 6,000 feet (about where the slope usually ends), 10,000 feet, or 20,000 feet deep. The slope is the wall of the ocean basin. Many geologists regard the continental shelf, beneath the shallow, next-to-shore waters, as part of the land. The continental slope is to them where the sea begins.

In some parts of the sea the continental slope falls away gradually from the shelf; elsewhere it falls steeply, around 300 feet to a mile. "However one looks at them," Robert C. Cowen writes in *Frontiers of the Sea*, "these are the greatest slopes and escarpments on the earth. There is nothing on land to rival them. Indeed, some of them are steeper and more awesome than the famous southern face of the Himalayas.

"Off the coast of South America, for instance, the east wall of the Peru-Chile Trench combines with the adjacent slopes of the Andes to give an average vertical rise of some 42,000 feet. That is practically twice the rise of the southern Himalayan slope. The greatest height difference known on the earth is found in this same ocean area where, at one point, the crustal surface rises from an undersea depth of 25,000 feet to a mountain height of 23,000 feet (in the Andes). This is a vertical rise of 48,000 feet (just over 9 miles) within a horizontal distance of 100 miles."

"Anyone," says C. P. Idyll in *Abyss*, "who has peered over the cliff at Glacier Park in Yosemite National Park, into the heart-stopping depth there, can appreciate these enormous drops; the distance from that mountaintop to the valley floor is only 3,254 feet." There is no mountainside on land that plunges anywhere near so deep as does the continental slope.

So far as human eyewitnesses are concerned, the continental slope is almost unknown and unexplored territory. The continental shelf, however, under only a shallow cover of water, is the best known part of the sea floor. Most of man's journeys to the bottom of the sea have been to the continental shelf. Individual divers are limited entirely to the shallow waters of the continental shelf. Only deep-diving submarines and bathyscaphes can descend to deeper depths, including the slope.

The continental slope is known for thick deposits of sediment. Down the slope the sediment sometimes spills as undersea landslides—turbidity currents. Animals on the slope include, off Japan, the hugest crab in the world—the long-legged Japanese spider crab, the largest arthropod (a joint-legged animal). It is 6 to 10 feet across its leg span and looks like a tremendous daddy longlegs. The American Museum of Natural History in New York has a specimen. The Japanese spider crab lives 3,300 feet beneath the sea, on the slope. Other slope animals often include glass sponges. They vary in height from a few inches to 2 or 3 feet. Some beautifully luminescent animals and fish inhabit the slope or water above it. Animals include a beautiful sea fan with plantlike arms, sea anemones in vast numbers, the long-stalked sea lilies, the polychaete worms in exquisite tubes, and, according to Richard Carrington in *A Biography of the Sea*, "giant sea spiders whose legs measure up to two feet long."

One of the few men who have seen the continental slope is Jacques-Yves Cousteau. "When," he wrote, "aboard a diving saucer, you reach the edge of the continental shelf, you are struck by the abruptness with which the floor of the sea suddenly drops off. Under the bright gleam of searchlights, the bottom disappears in the blue. You have to reason with yourself to fight off a feeling of dizziness. Then you tilt your bow down, on occasion as much as 30 to 35 degrees, to follow the slope downwards.

"The slanting surface often is furrowed by undersea canyons, abrupt and extremely narrow, which sometimes exhibit steps carved into their walls like giant staircases. Over such landscapes, the best echo sounders in the world are unable to transcribe what you see through the portholes of a diving saucer."

The first layman or civilian to go down and have a look at the continental shelf—the first man other than a scientist or hydronaut—probably was Walter Cronkite. In 1967 he dived to a depth of 2,500 feet in *Deepstar 4000*. He was over the slope. His comments, made to a private meeting in New York City, show how the continental slope looks to a man who is not an oceanographer. "All you see is desert," Mr. Cronkite said. The bottom appeared to be very fine dust.

He saw only a few animals. "In two hours on the bottom I saw only half a dozen living creatures," he said. "When the very rare creatures move across the slope, they leave dust clouds. The dust hangs there in the water, then settles slowly, like dust churned up by a covered wagon over 100 years ago."

He saw crabs. He saw a few "odd-looking fish with great eyes." He saw some odd eels—"miserable-looking creatures one and a half feet long, horribly ugly, with no faces, a mouth where their head should be." Recovered specimens of this eel have had two, three, four, or five hearts.

He was impressed by the fact that he had no depth perception. "I didn't know if a nearby fish was a whale a mile off or a minnow two feet away."

"The only growth there," he said, "is a spongelike growth on which someone had hung the sun-bleached rib cage of a cow. At least that's the way to describe it."

On Cronkite's dive to the continental slope, the *Deepstar* men found a current running at one-half to one knot due east, not west as had been thought. "Thus," Mr. Cronkite said, "theories about the currents in the Pacific Ocean may be blown sky-high. That was one of the important discoveries of our trip. Every trip down comes up with some contribution, so vast is the unknown on the bottom of the sea."

Two other men to eyewitness the sea floor at about the same depth one day saw it from *Deep Jeep*. *Deep Jeep* was built at the Navy's largest and most complete ordnance research and development center, the $300-million Naval Ordnance Test Station, China Lake, California. NOTS, in the beautiful Mojave Desert area, covers more than 1,200 square miles, or about the area of the state of Rhode Island, and has, in fact, become the largest defense laboratory in the western world. The Navy establishment was placed in the desert primarily to test airborne weapons. One that was developed there: the Sidewinder air-to-air missile, effective in Vietnam. Undersea weapons also are developed here—for example, the deep-running Torpedo Mark 46.

The two men in *Deep Jeep* made their trip in April, 1965. It was *Deep Jeep*'s first deep dive. She had however been tested and evaluated earlier by the Naval Ordnance Test Station with assistance from General Motors at Santa Barbara, California, and the Southwest Research Institute. Will Forman, who had designed *Deep Jeep*, piloted her. Forman's copilot was Commander Phil Johnson, United States Navy, later a fighter pilot commanding a carrier squadron off Vietnam. As her project manager, Forman sent me information on *Deep Jeep's* journey to the continental slope.

"Technically," Will Forman tells me, "we were on the San Clemente Escarpment, which is on the mainland side of San Clemente Island. The escarpment is on the opposite side of the island from the continental slope. I doubt if you could tell the difference from one side to the other since the island was pushed up from the sea floor."

Deep Jeep, a 5-foot-in-diameter, battery-powered steel sphere, with a viewport for her two men to peer through, is propelled and steered by two oil-flooded motors at a top speed of 2 knots. She has the capability of going 2,000 feet down. By far most research submarines descend 1,000 feet or less. So *Deep Jeep* has the added capacity of leaving the continental shelf and roaming the slope—at least the top part—to 2,000 feet down.

In the Pacific in April, 1965, she did.

"She is expected," said an Assistant Secretary of Defense in 1966, "to be highly useful in investigating the ocean's biological layer below 1,000 feet." That is an almost unknown depth for undersea explorers. *Deep Jeep*, he went on to say, "will also permit exploration of underwater canyons at greater depth and more extensively than before."

Deep Jeep can hover, turn on a dime, and had been, before her 2,000-foot dive, recovering experimental torpedoes from the bottom of the sea. "We had also conducted," Forman said, "mock submarine hatch join-ups (or nestings) as preliminary experiments related to future submarine rescue procedures." She was testing rescue procedure for the forthcoming Navy rescue submarines. "I was," says Forman, "on all the dives the *Jeep* made. She is now at Scripps, being refurbished for use by its scientists."

For her dive down to the San Clemente Escarpment, *Deep Jeep* had been flown in an Air Force C-124 from China Lake to San Clemente Island, a target area and training ground off the California coast for World War II amphibious forces. A Navy tender known as the *YFU 53* took *Deep Jeep* to sea. She was towed to an area where the sea floor, in this case the continental shelf, was 690 feet deep. At this point she descended to the bottom of the sea and began a long, slanting trip that took her down the continental slopelike escarpment to a point 2,000 feet beneath the surface.

"The first things observed upon reaching the bottom at about 700 feet down," *Deep Jeep's* trip memo says, "were numerous sea urchins, several red five-legged starfish, various flatfish, and guitarfish (shark)."

After a depth of 800 feet was reached, the slope turned very sharply downward. "From 800 feet on down," the memo reads, "the beginning of the escarpment [the slope] was indicated by banks or slopes reaching vertically 90 degrees on numerous occasions, but more frequently sloping from 60 to 80 degrees." Visibility was clear.

When the basalt rock outcrop area was reached, the two men in *Deep Jeep* saw rockfish. Octopuses were seen for the first time. "So," says the trip memo, "was the familiar gorgonian coral and sea plume.

"At about 1,100 feet, a rocket booster was observed, approximately 3 inches in diameter and 18 inches long, with one of the older type nozzles.

"On the basalt slopes, the outcrops were quite rugged, somewhat comparable to Last Chance Canyon near Mojave, California, in both slope and construction. There were boulders in several areas running from fist size to several feet in diameter."

Deep Jeep is equipped with ultraviolet light. It was used often as *Deep Jeep* prowled the escarpment. The men blinked it at the animals. "The ultraviolet light," they reported, "was flicked on at practically every biological specimen that went by or was encountered." The men expected the fish to glow, or light up. The fish didn't: "No fluorescence was observed."

What colors show up best in the depths under ultraviolet light? The answer is surprising. *Deep Jeep* took along a panel, coated with specially pigmented paints and connected near the ultraviolet light for reflection.

"An unexpected phenomenon occurred," says the trip memo. "Down to about 1,700 feet, the yellow wave length pigments seemed to be the most brilliant, but after going deeper the green became comparatively more vivid, reversing upon ascent. This was witnessed by both observers. The yellow and green were by far the most vivid of all the colors at the various depths."

"Below 1,800 feet," the two men reported, "many beautiful basket sponges looking like white funnels were observed, as well as shrimp and a few crabs; one area contained very small squid."

At the maximum depth of 2,010 feet that *Deep Jeep* reached, her ultraviolet light was turned on. The color card was dipped into the sand. "A dark brick red hue emanated, under the ultraviolet light, from the sand which had been silted onto the color card. This has been reported to be the effect of the calcium particles in the sand.

"The ultraviolet light was flicked on only when the visible lights could be turned off during the operation.

"On the ascent to the surface, where there was a better chance to use only the ultraviolet light since no visible light was necessary, there appeared what we refer to erroneously as fireflies, i.e., numerous passages of brilliant lighting. On several occasions, the visible lights were turned on in time to see that they were semitransparent material—plankton, presumably. They would light up everywhere within the view of our window in spite of the fact that some areas within our viewing cone [the cubic area of sea the men were looking at] were extremely remote from the ultraviolet lighting source."

The men thought that the ultraviolet light did not disturb the sea creatures. They may not see it. If so, with ultraviolet light it may be possible to observe life in the sea without its knowing it is being watched.

As *Deep Jeep* went up, the men encountered visible light from the daytime overhead—at as far as 750 feet down. The light at first was an aura. They had not expected to see the light till they were much higher. "This occurred," they said, "on a semi-overcast day at 1:30 non-daylight saving time." But Will Forman, while diving in the later search for the H-bomb, saw light even deeper. "I just got back from some dives in Spain," he wrote me in 1966, "and we observed light from 1,050 feet."

The men aboard *Deep Jeep* had one principal impression about the part of the San Clemente Escarpment they saw: It was steeper and more rugged than could be predicted from charts. "This leads us to believe," Will Forman said, "that much of the ocean bottom is far more rugged than has been pictured from sonar findings."

"Just as some geologists have been predicting," he concluded, "this leads to the unconfirmed belief that there exist many rugged ocean bottom areas that the existing charts often do not indicate."

The Bottom: "This Jules Verne World"

24

At 62, William Maurice Ewing looks back happily on 20 years spent aboard ships at sea trying to find out all he could about the bottom of the sea. "I have spent more time aboard ships," he says, "than at any other place I've ever lived."

Maurice Ewing, 6 feet 2 inches tall, his snowy hair tousled from years of sea winds, has a sailor's rolling gait and weather-beaten face. A professor of geology at New York City's Columbia University, and director of its Lamont Geological Observatory, he walks about the Columbia campus in the sneakers he wears to grip his heaving decks at sea. He wants to know how the earth was made. The best place to find out, he has believed for a generation, is the bottom of the sea, an area that in some places may be the primeval face of the earth. Years ago he set out to find what the bottom of the sea was like, and what was on it and under it. His researches have prepared the way for today's journeys to the bottom of the sea by men in deep-diving machines.

Jules Verne, who described the bottom of the sea graphically in fiction, died in 1905. Maurice Ewing, who would tell what the bottom of the sea is like in scientific detail, was born May 12 the next year in far-inland Lockney, Texas. His parents were Floyd and Hope Hamilton Ewing. Lockney is in the dusty plains in the north part of the state. There were no streams for the boy to swim in, and because he got only to paddle occasionally in a rain-filled mudhole, he did not become, and has not yet become, a good swimmer.

Today Ewing recalls his first look at the sea. He was a 16-year-old college freshman at Rice Institute (today University), Houston, when storm warnings were posted in Galveston, 50 miles away. Something—he does not know what—impelled him to go to watch. He stood on the seawall at Galveston and looked out.

"All I remember of that day in 1922," he says, "is that the waves were awfully big."

At Rice, Ewing learned physics. "Using the methods of physics to investigate the earth," he says, "led to a professorship in geology," his title at Columbia today. After Rice, Ewing became an instructor in physics at Lehigh University.

In 1934 the Geological Society of America called in Ewing, and gave him $2,000 (or about what it costs him today to keep a single research ship at sea for one day) to start the exploration of the oceans. Ewing says he had no special qualifications. It was simply that the Geological Society, he says, "thought oceanography was important work and was trying to stimulate young men to get going on it."

He got going. Since then Doc Ewing has explored the oceans aboard seagoing tugboats, fishing boats, PT boats, buoy boats, seaplane tenders, freighters, submarines, and research schooners including Woods Hole's *Atlantis*. Columbia University's own 202-foot-long, 533-ton diesel schooner *Vema*, acquired in 1952 and crammed with oceanographic gear, is a ship he has spent many years aboard. He tries to be aboard *Vema* during at least one leg of every one of her cruises, and in her he has sailed to the far reaches of the seas. "She can," says Ewing, "make any passage there is."

The *Vema* is the first oceanographic ship—and the first

ship in the world outside the United States Navy—permanently equipped to navigate by computer and by man-made satellite. The system was developed by the Applied Physics Laboratory of the Johns Hopkins University. J. Lamar Worzel, assistant to Ewing, says that it is of "revolutionary importance." It means *Vema* can know where she is within a matter of yards, not within a mile or a few miles as by the sun-and-stars system or even by shore-based electronic systems.

Ewing can take in stride, he says, his life at sea. "It is not frantic like the hard-pressed businessman's life ashore." He has been seasick only half a dozen times in his life. Sea explorers try to avoid storms in order to obtain calm weather so they can take cores or rocks from the bottom or tow nets for fish. Storms catch up with them anyway. One hurricane turned onto her beam-ends a ship Ewing was aboard. "The water in my porthole was black, not blue," he says. "Ships usually don't straighten up after they're over that far. They just roll on over." But the vessel did right herself.

Dwight D. Eisenhower, when president of Columbia, in 1948 appointed Maurice Ewing director of the Lamont Geological Observatory. This 125-acre Torrey Cliff estate, given by the widow of Thomas W. Lamont, the financier, is located amid trees on the top of the clifflike Palisades on the west bank of the Hudson River, about 20 miles up the river from New York City, on the way to West Point. Far below, on the bank, is Continental Can (formerly Gair) Pier, where *Vema* and other Columbia oceanographic ships put in. Doc Ewing, if he is at Lamont, meets every one as she returns from sea. A new one operated for the Navy is the *Robert D. Conrad*.

At sea, Ewing does essentially two things: (1) He listens—mainly to the echoes of sounds he has himself sent into the sea; and (2) he collects samples—samples of the water, of the animals in it, of the bottom, and of what's on and beneath the bottom of the sea.

Listening to echoes from his echo-sounders or from depth-

charge explosions tells Ewing how deep the sea is, and what the
bottom is made of—i.e., basalt or granite, and how much sediment covers it. From his measurements by depth charges comes
one of the mysteries of today's oceanography: In some places,
as in the Atlantic off Argentina, the sediment may be 2,000 or
3,000 feet thick. Yet the sediment, which consists of silt and
remains of sea creatures that have been drifting to the bottom
of the sea everywhere for millions of years, is completely missing in wide areas of the Pacific, Tahiti to Mexico. Ewing thinks
he will know why some day, but does not know so far.

Thick sediment may mean oil; Ewing finds what may be the
fields of the future in the middle of the Gulf of Mexico and the
Atlantic. Salt domes, believed to be of the type that have made
coastal Louisiana and Texas one of the richest oil areas in the
world, have been discovered by Ewing and other scientists
from Lamont on the bottom of the Gulf of Mexico. Lamont
has announced finding what may be 21 salt domes; located,
but not so far announced, 119 others.

With echo-sounding, Ewing and his associates have mapped
the undersea Mid-Atlantic Ridge. *Vema* and other Columbia
ships, with sounding, are said to "collect" undersea canyons,
they find so many; they have found them in all oceans. Some
are twice as big as the Grand Canyon, or even bigger. Some are
at the mouths of rivers, the Congo, the Ganges, the Indus, the
Hudson, and the Orinoco. Some are in mid-ocean. Columbia
men were the first to locate mid-ocean canyons. They find isolated mountains on the bottom of the sea. One off South Africa
recently discovered was over 15,000 feet tall from the abyss of
the Atlantic, taller than any United States mountain except in
Alaska. It rose to 120 feet beneath the surface, and if left uncharted could have wrecked a submarine. They found an extinct volcano 120 miles off New Jersey. Three miles down, on
the bottom, near Bermuda, Ewing and his brother, John,
planted a seismograph to detect earthquakes. Its batteries lasted
only a few days, but it reported an earthquake near Panama.
Other Ewing seismographs on land and beneath the sea have
shown that the Mid-Atlantic Ridge is an area of far more

earthquakes than was previously believed. The ridge also has many active volcanoes. Riding across the Arctic Ocean on a cake of ice, Columbia scientists listened to sound echoes and discovered a 5,000-foot-high mountain range beneath the sea, and a great plain, like the tablelands of the western United States, atop a huge submerged island.

In 1949 Ewing discovered that the earth's mantle lies only about 3½ miles below the sea floor, against 12 to 32 miles beneath the land; hence the possibility to drill through the earth's crust beneath the sea to see what's inside. Ewing, Bruce Heezen, and other Columbia scientists have shown that there is a continuous 45,000-mile-long crack, or rift, in the earth's crust on the bottom of the sea. It is a world-circling earthquake zone. The rift, from the Arabian Sea, connects with the famous African rift valleys. The rift runs down the Mid-Atlantic Ridge. Such a big crack tends to show that, as under a theory known as the continental drift, Europe and North America might be slowly moving away from each other. But the fact that the rift goes on into the Indian Ocean makes this assertion questionable. Besides individual mountains and canyons, and mountain ranges and the great rift, Ewing has studied the abyssal plains of the Atlantic.

What emerges from Columbia's bouncing sound (today usually blasts of high-pressure air) off the bottom of the sea is, the university says, "a 200,000-mile 'road map' of the sea bottom." It is a map that men in deep-diving submarines pore over.

Ewing takes samples of everything he can lay his hands on in the sea and beneath it. His samples help make by far the most complete picture of the depths and bottom of the sea men ever have had. Collecting samples of the water in the Aleutian Trench (near Alaska) in 1965 showed Columbia that, 18,000 to 22,000 feet down, there were deep-sea clouds: great turbid areas. Collecting a layer of chalk north of Wake Island, Columbia found the then oldest known material ever taken from the bottom of the sea. "This chalk," said Paul Cheminski of Columbia, "which contains microscopic fossils of planktonic foraminifera [minute animals that fish eat] of known age, was deposited during the upper part of the Cretaceous period about 106 million years ago."

Collecting a sample of a layer of clean white ash on the Pacific bottom off Ecuador told Columbia one of three things must have happened: (1) a collision of heavenly bodies; (2) a great volcanic eruption; or (3) the simultaneous explosion of many volcanoes. Collecting sediment far from shore, Columbia men find sand (which must come from the beach), land or shallow-water fossils, tree branches and leaves, and other debris of the land. From all these, they deduce that there are beneath the sea great landslides off the continental slopes or sides of sea mountains that become jet streams across the bottom of the sea. These jets—called turbidity currents—force their way through the depths and bury sea creatures—and may possess the awesome power to carve out the biggest canyons in the mid-ocean floor. A turbidity current, one day in 1929, may have snapped a dozen Atlantic cables, one after the other. If so, calculated from the times the cables parted, its speed some of the time was 50 m.p.h.

Collecting a whole lot of pebbles on the bottom between the Antarctic and Argentina, Columbia came up with quite a story: Penguins carry the pebbles in their craws (to grind up their food). Leopard seals eat the penguins. The seals excrete the pebbles. When Bruce Heezen and Bill Glass of Lamont found, they estimated, 300 million tons of material from outer space on the Pacific and Indian ocean bottom, they concluded that 700,000 years ago a heavenly body might have collided with the earth. What they found was microtektites, tiny glassy particles—shaped as cylinders, teardrops, pears, balls, or dumbbells—four-hundredths of an inch in diameter. They thought that the awesome crash might have changed the polarity of the earth—i.e., before it, compass needles (if any had existed) would have pointed to the South Pole.

Columbia scientists send down nets and trawls to all depths, from surface to the bottom of the sea. They collect specimens of ordinary, rare, and unknown animals. They have caught bright blue shrimps, sponges, fish with long feelers, and brilliant red, previously unknown, starfish. They once captured a fish whose lower jaw slid in and out like a desk drawer.

They have hauled in many a fish largely composed of huge mouth and snaky body. Fish with their tails drawn out to long points are characteristic of the abyssal depths. The rattails are an example.

On rock pulled up from the bottom they find fully grown octopuses, about an inch long. "We may get little octopuses," Ewing said to me, "when we dredge up rock. Their bodies are one-half inch in diameter, their tentacles three-quarters of an inch in length."

In 1965 Ewing was obtaining photos with cameras lowered by cable from as far as six miles down (no vehicle except bathyscaphes, and not even all of them, can go that deep). The pictures showed signs of life. "There is always," Ewing's brother, John, told me, "some kind of queer track or burrow. Sometimes there are holes or anthills or mounds on the bottom."

As pictures of the bottom of the deep sea were made in increasing numbers, a major puzzle appeared in many of them. There were totally unfamiliar animal tracks that often showed up. The tracks were large coils from about 1 foot to 6 feet in diameter. The pictures never showed the beginning or the end of the coils. The *Vema* photographed the tracks in depths greater than two miles and in nearly every ocean-bottom area surveyed on a trip between Wellington, New Zealand, and Tahiti. Then the U.S.N.S. *Eltanin*, a National Science Foundation ocean-exploring ship that for the past few years has been operating between South America and the Antarctic, photographed the mysterious trail in the bottom areas in the Southwest Pacific and in the Scotia Sea.

"Still more 'spirals,' about twenty," Columbia University said, "have been found in pictures from the North Atlantic, Indian Ocean, and North Pacific." But the South Pacific seemed a good place for them.

All in all, the mysterious coils that went round and round in the bottom of the sea were a puzzle: They made marine zoologists go round and round in frustration. They could not guess what animal made them.

Then a camera lowered to 15,534 feet, or nearly three miles, beneath the Pacific, got a picture that showed the coil. Only this time, inside the coil, was the animal that made it: a "giant" (3 feet long) enteropneust, or acorn worm. This is a worm-shaped (more or less) creature. If you are not familiar with it, do not be surprised. The photo of the acorn worm was the first deep-sea record of it since the *Challenger* expedition in 1873 dredged up three damaged specimens in the Atlantic; and *Challenger's* acorn worms were the very first men had ever seen or known about. Bruce Heezen and Donald W. Bourne of Cambridge University were the men who got the picture that solved the mystery.

Columbia deep-sea photographers thought they had another new creature when they pictured a TV-antenna-shaped animal on the bottom. Tony Amos told me about it at the Lamont Observatory. Then they located the creature: They found it in the *Challenger* reports of almost 100 years ago. It is a sponge.

By today, Dr. Ewing has put together a much more complete picture of the bottom of the sea than Jules Verne had. It is quite a picture: Volcanoes belching lava. "Hot rock," Ewing says, "from volcanoes or fissure flows." Undersea mountain ranges, and tall isolated mountains, with steep and gentle slopes, cliffs, terraces, and buttresses. Deep piles of sediment—or only bare rock. The seas above the bottom inhabited by strange and weird fish. Landslides—jet streams—racing down and carrying boulders across the sea floor. Turbidity currents that can carve the earth's greatest canyons in the bottom of the sea. Ewing, who never has found time to read *20,000 Leagues Under the Sea*, nevertheless refers to the bottom of the sea, especially around the Mid-Atlantic Ridge, as "this Jules Verne world."

In 1964 Ewing was head of Operation Deepscan, which sent

the French bathyscaphe *Archimede* on ten journeys to the deepest bottom of the Atlantic. She went down into the 450-mile-long, over-27,000-feet deep Puerto Rico Trench.

"The *Archimede* 'sat' on the bottom," Ewing said, "part of the way down the south wall of the trench, and then traveled about one-and-one-half miles."

On a dive to the deepest part in the trench, over five miles down, the humidity inside *Archimede* crept up to 100 percent and the heat to 95 degrees Fahrenheit. Bread in sandwiches felt like a well-soaked sponge.

Archimede's crew—Commander Georges Houot of the French Navy, Professor Jean Peres, and Dr. Henri Delauze—saw giant steps in both walls of the Puerto Rico Trench. They found currents unknown before. At the very bottom they observed fish 1 to 5 inches long. Said Peres, "They are pinky white and swim around like tendrils." It was the first time deep bathyscaphe diving had come to the Atlantic.

"What was interesting to me," said Allyn Vine, who dived aboard *Archimede* into the trench, "were the marks on the bottom. There was no space as big as a tabletop without a footprint or a dimple from a pebble or a mark of some kind.

"We found skate at twenty thousand feet, almost four miles down. The skate tried to swim away from us and swam in front of the window for one and a half minutes. The pilots had seen skates at many depths, but this was the deepest yet. Possibly the skate is found at all depths.

"The crew sat the *Archimede* down on the bottom, stopped, and had a big lunch—salads, chicken goodies, and half an hour of conversation."

At a narrow part of the trench at one moment, Vine said, the *Archimede's* pilot heard a voice from his right saying to move away from the rocks. Simultaneously, a voice from his left said to move away from the rocks. "I went straight up" the pilot said. "Fast."

In December, 1966, Columbia University scientists announced perhaps their most surprising discovery of all: that "the floors of the ocean are in systematic and surprisingly rapid motion."

The report by Dr. James R. Heirtzler, senior research associate, and Walter C. Pitman III, research assistant, appeared in the December 2, 1966, issue of *Science*, of the American Association for the Advancement of Science. Heirtzler, 41, and his staff of 25 at the Lamont Observatory, had gathered the world's largest collection of marine geomagnetic data.

What happens may be something like this: From the interior of the globe, over geological ages, hot rock moves upward. The hot rock climbs to the bottom of the sea beneath mid-ocean mountain ranges including the Mid-Atlantic Ridge. From beneath either side of such a ridge, the rock spreads out on the ocean floor. The rock, now the bottom of the sea, may move, or spread, at a rate of 2 inches a year, a speed equal to that of some glaciers.

"I believe," Dr. Heirtzler said, "we're on the verge of realizing one of the major goals of the marine geophysicist: the ability to reconstruct the complete history of the world's oceans." He added: "That the earth's crust is in smooth but large scale flow requires a rewriting of many geophysics and geology texts."

The discovery of the moving sea floor was followed by a sweeping theory:

Beneath the sea floor, and beneath the land, deep inside the interior of the earth, there is what amounts to a natural atomic energy plant. It is a huge one. The theory was put forth at the end of 1967 by two Columbia University scientists, David B. Ericson and Goesta Wollin in a book, *The Ever-Changing Sea*.

Inside the globe, the theory says, nuclear reactions take place. They create heat in rock as far as 1,800 miles deep inside the crust of the earth. More heat comes from the intensely-hot fluid core of the earth. As the rock inside heats up, it becomes lighter, and the rock pushes outward through the interior of the globe in gigantic circles. The process of the rock flowing through the interior of the earth is a slow one over the millions of years that measure geological time: The flow is estimated at an inch a year.

The hot material pushes upward to the crust of the earth, where, near the earth's surface, it spreads out—and takes the place of cooler material that sinks. This rock flow, itself caused by the nuclear furnace at its beginning, in turn causes—Ericson and Wollin say—volcanoes to burst forth, mountains to rise, rift valleys to open, and shallow seas to drain from the continents. The rock flow pushed up the continents, the theory goes, and more than 100 million years ago broke them into several parts. The rock flow is pushing the parts apart today (continental drift). The authors believe that their theory is the solution to "the most critical problem confronting earth scientists": What is the source of the energy that makes mountains and controls geological revolutions? The theory goes a long way to answer Maurice Ewing's question as to how the earth was made.

Nuclear reactions inside the earth are suggested, the writers say, by the discovery of the prevalence of nuclear isotopes of various common elements.

The flow of hot rock outward from deep within the globe is called convection currents. "To explain the origin of continents, and ocean basins, the convection theory," say Ericson and Wollin, "seems to us to be the most satisfactory because it can explain in a consistent way not only the major but also the minor features on the earth's surface." They view the continents except Antarctica as a single island being split apart: That the continents were once a single land mass, they say, is indicated by the fact that you can travel to all the continents except Antarctica without at any time having to cross more than 60 miles of sea.

Maurice Ewing and Columbia's Lamont Geological Observatory have put oceanography—exploring the oceans—on a full-time basis. So have other United States oceanographic institutions and universities. No nation before the United States ever had put oceanography on a full-time schedule, collecting facts around the clock, around the year, a mass production of knowledge about the sea. The old way was to send out an exploring ship once in a while. This was inefficient. Lamont and today's other major oceanographic institutions keep their ships out all the time: exploring, exploring, exploring; learning, learning, learning. As a result, new facts are today pouring in, facts the deep-diving explorers of the bottom of the sea are finding invaluable.

In 1960 Ewing was awarded the first Vetlesen Prize for achievement in the earth sciences—geophysics, oceanography, seismology, others—an award established to be the equivalent of the Nobel prizes in other fields. Britain's Royal Geographic Society says of Ewing: "The scientific achievements of the man himself and his co-workers are enormous. . . . There are no oceans where Lamont scientists have not been working." "I have not," Doc Ewing says in what must be the most remarkable understatement of his generation, "thought about much of anything except the sea since 1934."

Ewing actually has made one voyage as a passenger. He sailed aboard a freighter. He was taking a vacation. But Ewing persuaded the skipper to let him run the echo-sounder. With it, off the Grand Banks, he measured the depths and got a profile of the bottom of the sea and, as a result, he knew the Grand Banks were part of the North American continental shelf, and not of the abyss of the Atlantic.

"Not to have run the echo-sounder," says Dr. Ewing, "would have been like closing your eyes at the circus."

The Invitation to Davy Jones's Locker

25

If the new deep-diving submarines and men in the sea already have made many of the adventures depicted by Jules Verne come true, they can be expected in the future to far excel anything he imagined.

There will be more of both the submarines and the men. They will make more and deeper dives, including many into that always forbidding, dreaded, and hitherto inaccessible-to-man area: the abyss of the oceans, the mid-ocean floor. They will enter the great trenches in the bottom of the sea. They eventually will range anywhere and everywhere over the bottom of the sea.

The biggest of the deep-diving submarines, *Aluminaut*, has a schedule for the next few years that will mean she will sail far beyond the 20,000 leagues (60,000 miles) of Jules Verne's *Nautilus*.

Aluminaut has an inside diameter of 7 feet, can be operated by two or three men, and can carry as many as six or more. This means that *Aluminaut* can invite you—scientists or anyone else —along for a deep dive. The line is forming, and all you have to do is buy a ticket. It is expensive, but it is like buying a ticket for a trip to the moon on an Apollo spaceship: The trip itself was not possible at all until the late 1960's, at any price.

Aluminaut does invite passengers. She normally will carry three or four on each dive. And she will dive in every ocean, visit countries all over the world, and be available to passengers in many lands. She will give many a person his first trip to the bottom of the sea. She will do for hundreds of people what the *Nautilus* did for Professor Arronax—long considered so fantastic that it was not conceivable the human race ever could make it come true.

Among other things, *Aluminaut* hopes to make even deeper dives than her own record of 6,250 feet. She'll try, says Art Markel, vice president of Reynolds Sub-Marine Services Corporation, a dive of 9,000 feet outside and to the eastward of the Tongue of the Ocean, on the seaward side of the Bahama Banks.

"There's a lot of interest in the geology of the bottom here," he says, "on the part of scientists."

The plan is for *Aluminaut* to dive to 9,000 feet, with three to four passengers aboard, and then to inch along the sea floor. She will try to reach her capacity depth of 15,000 feet when, and if, she gets a contract that requires it. When she does, the pressure of the sea almost three miles down will shorten her by 1 inch. At that depth, *Aluminaut* will be approximately as far below sea level as the summit of the highest mountain in the United States outside Alaska—Mount Whitney, California, 14,495 feet—is above it. And approximately as far below as the summit of Europe's highest mountain, Mont Blanc, between France and Italy, 15,771 feet. Because a league (as in *20,000 Leagues*) is three miles, *Aluminaut* at 15,000 feet will be almost one league beneath the surface.

Since her 6,250-foot dive, *Aluminaut* never has been deeper than 5,000 feet, often has gone to 4,500, and most often to the 3,000-foot level. Many future dives will be at these depths. The shorter the dive you take, the less it will cost: the price of your ticket is figured in part according to the number of feet you dive. The price may run about 50 cents a foot. Thus, you might pay $1,500 for a 3,000-foot dive, or $4,500 for a voyage to the bottom of the sea 9,000 feet beneath the surface. Besides the dive, you will get undersea photographs made on your trip and a tape recording of comments made during it. Your souvenirs, that is, will be sound and pictures. You may also get TV films. *Aluminaut* carries a TV camera mounted on her bow. It takes pictures as she cruises along. *Aluminaut* can play back the pictures at once—like instant replays of track meets or football games. This quick second glance helps when a sea monster, for instance, is seen and must be identified.

Dives to 3,000 to 4,500 feet will be made, according to the Reynolds Metals Company's announcement of *Aluminaut's* plans, on the eastern coast of the Gulf of Mexico and in the Atlantic to the Blake Plateau, near the Bahamas, off the Florida Keys, and in the Straits of Florida.

Other dives will be made off New England, to the Grand Banks, off Newfoundland, and to the Gulf of Aden, in the Middle East. Art Markel wants to get into the Indian Ocean. "No deep-diving submarine ever has," he explains. "The Indian Ocean looks interesting." He plans to explore the Mediterranean near where Carthage once was. "It is," he says, "a graveyard of ancient ships."

You can, if you want to, book your passage on a dive especially looking for minerals (the Blake Plateau) or observing the fish (possibly the Grand Banks) or looking for calico scallops and royal red shrimps (off Cape Canaveral, Florida), or studying geology (*Aluminaut* plans to climb the undersea Bahama Escarpment near Bimini). You can even buy a ticket on a trip that will drift along beneath the Gulf Stream at down to 1,500 feet, much as Jacques Piccard plans in the *PX-15*. *Aluminaut* already has drifted 25 miles at 1,000 feet beneath the Gulf Stream. And on a 33-hour-trip submerged she cruised 70 miles across the Gulf Stream from the Grand Bahama Banks to Miami.

There is, said Professor Arronax in *20,000 Leagues*, "an

under-current, which empties into the basin of the Atlantic, through the Straits of Gibraltar, the surplus waters of the Mediterranean." The *Nautilus* sailed, in this undersea current, into the Atlantic.

"This—the Straits of Gibraltar—are real interesting," Art Markel said to me. "The study of the tidal flow and outflow through the Straits of Gibraltar has both military and scientific value." He plans for *Aluminaut* to cruise just above the bottom through the straits and thus study the movement of the water where it happens.

The *Nautilus* sailed between Arabia and Africa in the Red Sea. Markel tells me that plans are for *Aluminaut* to do that. Only one real-life deep-diving submarine has preceded her into the Red Sea. That was the *Soucoupe,* or diving saucer, belonging to Jacques-Yves Cousteau. In the Red Sea, in 1963, she had her own base on the bottom of the sea—the first submarine ever to have a sea-floor base. It was a garage, a steel dome. Compressed breathing gas kept out the seawater. The diving saucer popped up inside the compressed air in the dome to let out the two men in her crew and to have her batteries recharged. Two nearby similar small buildings, also full of compressed gas, provided living quarters for men on the sea floor. In the tiny village of three structures, Cousteau's Conshelf II (for *Con*tinental *Shelf*) experiment, you could see a forerunner of bigger towns and even cities on the bottom of the sea.

Markel and *Aluminaut* will explore the bottom of the Red Sea for valuable minerals. About 7,000 feet down in a Red Sea submarine valley, off the continental shelves of Arabia and the Sudan on the African continent, the surface research ship *Chain* has found what may be a lode of gold, silver, zinc, and copper whose worth may be far greater than that of the metal (silver and lead) ore taken from the Coeur d'Alene region in Idaho since the 1870's. In addition, there is abundant manganese and iron in the Red Sea deposit.

The *Chain* belongs to Woods Hole. Supported by the National Science Foundation, in the fall of 1966, she spent six weeks in the Red Sea. The nearest city to her operating area was Juddah, the port of the Mohammedans' sacred city, Mecca, in Saudi Arabia. Her scientists collected about 70 core samples—tubes of the sediment and mud on the bottom of the Red Sea. The United States Geological Survey estimated, from the core samples, that there is $1.5 billion worth of gold, silver, zinc, and copper in only the top 30 feet of the sea bottom in but one of three areas sampled by the *Chain*. The dried residue of the core samples was about 90 percent heavy metal sulfides and oxides. The most abundant were zinc, copper, iron, and manganese. The chairman of the Woods Hole department of chemistry, Dr. John M. Hunt, chief scientist on the *Chain* in the Red Sea, said later the discovery was the "most concentrated ore deposit of underwater minerals that has been found to date anywhere." Says Art Markel: "A few measurements by oceanographic vessels have indicated a tremendous amount of minerals."

There are believed to be other vast deposits of minerals on the bottom of the sea. They may be most often found, as is the one in the Red Sea, along rift valleys—cracks in the earth's crust like the seams in a tennis ball. Along these cracks, oceanographers believe, heat and gases boil upward from the interior of the globe to the bottom of the sea. Minerals may be developed by the heat and chemistry of the process.

In *20,000 Leagues*, the *Nautilus* comes upon a hot spot on the bottom of the sea. "The panels opened," said Professor Arronax (so he could look through the windows in the *Nautilus*), "and I saw the sea entirely white all round. A sulphurous smoke was curling amid the waves, which boiled like water in a copper. I placed my hand on one of the panes of glass, but the heat was so great that I quickly took it off again."

Aluminaut on the bottom of the Red Sea, in the area where the mineral deposit is located, can sail into hot water.

Woods Hole's former research vessel *Atlantis*, a sailing ship, found the hot water by lowering thermometers: a hole in the waist of the Red Sea where the bottom water reached

205

a temperature of 77 degrees Fahrenheit, with cooler water on top of it.

Chain; Atlantis II, the new Woods Hole oceanographic vessel; *Discovery*, the British research ship; and *Meteor*, a German vessel with G. Dietrich as chief scientist, all have found hot water in several deeps on the bottom of the Red Sea. The water may be almost as hot as that in a kitchen faucet.

Said J. C. Swallow of the National Institute of Oceanography in Great Britain, who was along on the *Discovery:* "When water was being drawn from bottles that had been near the bottom it seemed to run out more slowly than usual, and any that got spilt on deck immediately dried up, leaving a thick white patch of crystals."

The hot water showed a salinity of ten times that of normal seawater. "This," said Dr. Paul M. Fye, the president and director of Woods Hole, "is comparable with the water of the Dead Sea and considerably saltier than that of Great Salt Lake."

The hot water is unusually acid. "Both deeps," said Dr. Fye, "are anaerobic, judged by the absence of free oxygen and the presence of heavy metals in their fully reduced stage."

The sediment cores from the deeps were tarry black—and composed mainly of iron oxides, anhydrite, and amorphous silica. X-ray patterns revealed small amounts of sphalerite (an ore of zinc). Samples of water in the deeps, taken by *Atlantis II*, showed a few hundred to a few thousand times the concentration of iron, manganese, and silica found in the open ocean.

There are mysteries surrounding the hot spots on the Red Sea floor. We don't know how the hot salty water originates. We don't know why there are the concentrates of iron, manganese, and silica in the areas. We don't know the chemical relationship between the hot brine and the deposits of silica, anhydrite, and heavy metals.

The high salt content in the water of the hot spots, the National Geographic Society says, anchors the water to the bottom; the sunken holes or pools on the bottom of the Red

Sea may hold, the society estimates, 50,000 times the normal concentrations of heavy metals—gold, silver, iron, and copper.

Dr. Fye calls these hot spots on the bottom of the Red Sea, "surely a major scientific discovery." Says he, "We will have to return to study this brew of interesting chemicals in the near future."

Aluminaut in the hot water on the bottom of the Red Sea will contribute, too.

Other *Aluminaut* dives will be near Surtsey, a brand-new volcanic island that recently pushed up through the surface of the ocean near Iceland; to the Reykjanes Plateau, between Greenland and the Faeroes; in the North Sea; between Newfoundland and England to a terrace that, like the Blake Plateau and the Red Sea deeps, may contain minerals; and eventually into the Pacific.

For her trips, *Aluminaut*, which had made over 200 dives by 1968, will have a new tender vessel that can take her anywhere in the world. A model of the tender, as this book was written, was tested at the Stevens Institute, Hoboken, New Jersey. "She will be a ship," Art Markel says, "with a large open slot in her stern. The *Aluminaut* will enter the slot. A lift device will pick her up—all 70 tons of her—and put her onto a cradle on wheels."

Captain Nemo of Jules Verne's *Nautilus* found treasure on the bottom of the sea. In Vigo Bay, Spain, where a treasure fleet had been burned and scuttled, he found "ingots of gold and silver, cascades of piastres and jewels."

On the subject of treasure ships, Markel is reserved in his comments. This may be because there have been so many fruitless hunts for treasure in the past. But it was he who saw that well-preserved galleon on the bottom of the Mediterranean. And he does believe that the sea, below the top zone where sunlight penetrates, preserves the ships that have sunk, and a good part of their contents. The Reynolds Metals Company even invites you to book your passage in *Aluminaut* to look for yourself. One of its news releases begins, "Interested in spotting old shipwrecks lying in water some 3,000 feet deep off the southern coast of the United States?" "There are still treasure ships," Markel said to me with a chuckle in his voice. "We think we know where one is."

The Future on the Bottom of the Sea

26

The exploration of the depths and bottom of the sea is by far the biggest job of exploration ever undertaken on earth. "The sea," Jules Verne wrote, "is everything. It covers seven-tenths of the terrestrial globe." The distance across the Pacific Ocean is 11,000 miles, or almost one-half the circumference of the earth. The vastness of the Pacific Ocean is indicated by one statistic from the *Guinness Book of World Records:* "The world's most distant point from land is a spot in the South Pacific, approximately 48° 30′ S, 125° 30′ W, which is about 1,660 miles from the nearest points of land, namely Pitcairn Island, Ducie Island, and Cape Dart, Antarctica. Centered on this spot, therefore, is a circle of water with an area of about 8,657,000 square miles—about 7,000 square miles larger than the U.S.S.R., the world's largest country."

The top half of the globe (north of the equator) is three-fifths ocean. The bottom (southern) half is four-fifths ocean. "The face of the earth," says the Bureau of Commercial Fisheries, Honolulu, "is essentially a single ocean—interrupted by islands that range in size from a single volcanic peak thrusting up from the floor of the deep to the vast bulwark of Eurasia."

The bottom of this ocean is 139 million square miles in area.

Between the surface and the bottom, there are 330 million cubic miles of water to explore. This volume of water is as great as the volume of the moon. The volume is 18 times the volume of all land above sea level. It is 97 percent of the water on earth (the rest is lakes, rivers, and ice). There are 1.6 billion billion tons of seawater. They weigh 3 quintillion tons.

"If the water of all the oceans were poured into gigantic cube-shaped vessels measuring a mile in each direction," Richard Carrington writes in *A Biography of the Sea*, "these vessels, if laid end to end, would span the distance between the earth and the sun nearly four times."

"While one cubic mile is a mere drop in the ocean," Gerald Wendt wrote in UNESCO *Courier* for November, 1954, "a cubic mile is so large that the entire human race could be packed into less than 1/10th of it."

The job of exploring the oceans has scarcely begun. "Of the bottom of the sea," the National Geographic Society said as recently as May, 1965, "95 percent has not been accurately charted." "Only about 2 percent of the deep-sea floor," Dr. Roger Revelle said not long ago, "has been even moderately surveyed. As far as our understanding of the sea floor is concerned, we are about where we were a hundred years ago in surveying the land."

A hundred years ago the United States was opening its West, and discovering all the West's resources. Opening the sea may prove of similar usefulness to mankind. "What vast resources and potential may exist in this [ocean]," says *Ocean Science and Technology*, a pamphlet from Lafayette College, Easton, Pennsylvania, "until recent decades considered completely inhospitable, and largely unknown to man."

"The sea rush is on," said a National Geographic News Bulletin for September 13, 1967. "Oceanographers predict that, in time, industry will use everything in the ocean but the roar of the surf." Out of the seawater itself men already are obtaining salt, fresh water, magnesium, calcium, and bromine. Iodine and Epsom salts come from the sea or from brine. In the future, many more minerals and drugs may come from seawater (or sea plants or animals). One item: We may learn how to use the superb glue that barnacles hang onto ships with—to hold in the fillings in your teeth. Almost all of the elements are in seawater, many of them, such as gold, in quantities too small to be economically separated out of the water at the present time. When a bromine plant, for instance, processed 15 tons of seawater, gold worth only one-one-thousandth of a cent was recovered. Another use of seawater, from the National Geographic News Bulletin: ". . . sea water may become a fantastic fount of nuclear power. If a hydrogen furnace could be developed to harness the power of the H-bomb, its fuel would be heavy hydrogen, or deuterium. The most plentiful source of deuterium is the sea."

Other sources of energy from the sea may be found in harnessing the tides or making use of the differences in temperature between warm and cool layers of water. Besides minerals in the water itself, there are minerals (manganese, iron, others) on the bottom. There are minerals (gold, silver, oil, gas, sulfur, copper, and bauxite) beneath the bottom.

To do the biggest exploring job on earth, Americans are making big preparations. A new exploring submarine—with nuclear power—shortly will be prowling the bottom. The *NR-1*, she will be able to remain submerged indefinitely, as can our military nuclear submarines. Says Vice-President Hubert Humphrey: "With the unlimited endurance of nuclear power, *NR-1* will have a capability unmatched by any research vehicle now in operation or envisioned."

The Bureau of Commercial Fisheries thinks that just such a nuclear submarine as the *NR-1*, able to prowl the depths, locate (through viewing ports and TV) schools of fish, and follow them indefinitely, would be ideal for finding great stocks of fish men don't catch, because they don't know where to look for them. We are, for instance, catching the old skipjack tuna in the Pacific—but so far have not found the young or middle-aged tuna, which must be there if the old ones are.

If the *NR-1* develops speed comparable to or better than that rumored for other nuclear submarines—say 20, 30, or 40 knots—she will be the first deep-diving research submarine ever to be able to keep up with those greatest of undersea monsters, the whales. The sperm whale travels at up to 12 knots. A school of black whales, or pilot whales, not long ago circled a Navy ship traveling at 22 knots (25 miles an hour), and kept on circling the ship for several days. A man in fine physical shape, the Navy says, could spend energy at a comparable rate two to four hours. How the pilot whale keeps it up for days eludes us. The blue, or sulfur-bottom whale, at 150 tons and up to 100 feet long the biggest animal that ever lived on land or sea, can go about as fast. The blue whale is 35 times as big as an elephant, and huger by far than any dinosaur that ever existed. It has a tongue that weighs 3½ tons. It wiggles 20 tons of muscles at the stern of its spine to develop 500 horsepower, and push it along at a top speed of 22 knots. If the *NR-1* does keep up with whales, she may not only find where they roam and learn more about their habits, she may also help bring about a day when men will raise whales in pods (a pod is a school or herd of whales) and round them up with submarines. This, some scientists predict, will be a new source of meat.

The *NR-1* might carry the first men ever to see the giant squid (60 feet long) alive in its own habitat (swimming 1,500 or more feet beneath the surface). The ten-armed monster never has been intentionally caught. It has been accidentally dragged up, once or twice, in fishermen's nets, and sometimes washed ashore.

From such rare events we know the great squid has tremendous eyes (the diameter of a 33⅓-r.p.m. record), arms as thick as a man's thigh, with 200 or more vacuum-cup suckers on each arm, and claws both inside and around the suckers. The giant squid may weigh as much as two tons. It is a fearsome creature, and its battles with the 70-foot-long sperm whale are believed to be the most ferocious battles between monsters on earth. The fights are rarely seen—they occur in the depths; we know, because we find the squid in sperm whales' stomachs and the scars of the squid's tentacles on the whale's skin. Men in the *NR-1*—or in the *Alvin, Aluminaut, Deepstar, Deep Quest,* or *Deep Diver*—might be the first explorers in history to see a battle of the undersea giants.

From the *NR-1* and other deep-diving submarines there will be more observations and more spectacular sights. Kenneth V. Mackenzie of the Naval Undersea Warfare Center, San Diego, after making trips aboard *Trieste* and *Deepstar,* described an ocean full of life: "When we dive, we observe many organisms and much debris—which are commonly called snow. These conditions have been observed whenever dives have been made. It is as if the ocean were a living organism." At 2,500 feet down in the Loma sea valley, off California, John Beagles looked out *Deepstar's* viewports and saw a bottom covered with inverted cones. There were two or three holes at the base of each cone. "Then," he said, "I saw a wavy arm coming out of one of the holes. We stopped to see what was going on and observed a large red ophiuroid (a brittle star) was in each of the holes. It appeared as if the ophiuroid would come up and wave arms around as if sampling the current and then go back. Whether the ophiuroid makes the holes and lives in them or whether they are occupying spaces made by other burrowing organisms is not known."

On June 19, 1967, off Great Stirrup Cay, Bahamas, men aboard the submarine *Deep Diver* went to the bottom, got out, and watched the mating of squid. I. E. Wallen of the Smithsonian Institution coordinated the project, and F. E. Roper of the Smithsonian identified the squid. *Deep Diver* settled to the bottom in 30 feet of water. A diver stepped out onto the sea floor. "In a short time, thousands of squid, in great activity, appeared in the area illuminated by the lights. The cephalopods were densely concentrated near the bottom, although some were as much as 15 feet above the bottom. At first impressed by the enormous number of squid, their graceful motion and iridescent hues, we soon realized that this was not an aimless performance but a mass mating phenomenon. With few exceptions, the squid were paired off, and, at any given time, several dozen pairs could be seen mating." On a second dive, June 26, the mating again was observed; on both nights, mates had been established at the start—no courting was seen. The squid did not feed on dwarf herring or big-eyed scad seen on the second dive; a barracuda, on the first dive, was seen to attack stray squid. Four egg capsules removed the same night as spawned contained respectively 212, 233, 261, and 291 eggs. Several egg capsules removed a week after they were spawned contained active embryos about 3 millimeters long. The embryos had large eyes. They were swimming inside the egg. With well-developed funnels, they "sporadically propelled themselves around inside the gelatinous capsule."

"I am always exhilarated by each dive," says a letter to me from Ken Mackenzie, a man who at one time or another has held the records for the deepest dives in both Atlantic and Pacific (made aboard the bathyscaphe *Trieste*). "There is always the unexpected to see. We always see life—and that was impossible by the experts until recently. Now they have an abundance of bottom photographs and direct observations. As you cruise on the bottom you never know what will be next. On two dives to four thousand feet off the Coronado Islands in 1966 we approached two different unexploded submarine depth charges. We photographed both at a distance of eight feet. I made some studies at a depth of three thousand feet, west of San Diego. It was just like being in a large fairyland garden. There were large orange and yellow lilies, smaller white ones, orange starfish, purple and pink anemones attached to the lilies. There were sablefish, hagfish (with three hearts) and others, worm tubes, beautiful fans. It was breathtaking as one approached patch after patch. It was hard to believe that all these flowers (the lilies, anemones, fans) were all animals."

"Every time we go down there we see something new," says Bob Bradley, the *Deepstar* pilot. "You never see the same situation twice," Ron Church chimes in. "There is a distinct difference in marine life everywhere you dive. A different variety will live at a spot just two miles away from one type of fish, and different varieties live at different depths." "The potential is enormous," says D. K. Ela, *Deepstar* program manager, "for geological, archaeological, and biological studies. Submersibles can investigate the bottom structure and the water between the bottom and the surface. And if we're ever going to exploit resources in the ocean—oil, fish harvests, minerals—then the ocean bottom has to be surveyed."

Jim Cooney had said to me, "Everything in oceanography is unexpected." On a *Deepstar* dive, Dr. Robert F. Dill saw a bottom covered with cobblestones—and no dredge had brought up cobblestones from that point. "Now," he says, "we must question indirect dredging from the surface." From the diving saucer, chief pilot Albert Falco saw the unexpected: "It's a little fish," he exclaimed, "that comes out of the sand, and stands on its tail. Hey, it's digging in by its tail. It's gone underground." Scuba divers from the Miami Seaquarium later saw the same entrancing performance: an entrance into its burrow in the bottom of the sea tail first by the rare, 4-inch-long, pearl-colored jawfish.

Peering through the *Alvin's* viewports, John Schlee of the United States Geological Survey found the unexpected: He was impressed by the steepness of bottom-of-the-sea slopes where fine-grained sediment accumulates and stays without sliding off. In the Tongue of the Ocean he found sediment stable on slopes from 23 to 76 degrees. He reported his observations in the April, 1967, *Geotimes*, of the American Geological Institute, and said the sediment is "cohesive with depth" and worked by burrowing animals.

Schlee described a trip down in the *Alvin:* "There was no sensation of motion; only the fading light outside, the steady climb of the depth-gauge needle, and the movement of bioluminescent plankton past the ports gave any indication of the descent. The surface water was clear and greenish blue. At four hundred feet down, the water was a dull blue-green, and at eight hundred feet it was a deep greenish-gray. A thousand feet below the surface, a dark gray light filtered through the side ports; between eleven hundred and fourteen hundred feet it gave out entirely. However, by looking straight up through the small port in the hatch cover, we found daylight discernible to two thousand feet."

The *Alvin* approached the bottom (5,500 feet) with all outside lights on. "With approximately forty feet showing on the Fathometer, I noticed a lightening of the green haze, and then the haze became mottled as the sea floor came into view. About fifteen to twenty feet from the bottom, the water cleared and there before us was a pale olive-gray carpet of carbonate sediment dotted with dark purple holothurians." There were burrow holes of animals on the bottom. There were many animal tracks crisscrossing the bottom; "one set formed a pattern like intestinal loops."

Schlee saw a cliff ahead, at least 50 feet high. He could not see the top. "The whole scene could best be pictured by imagining a series of steep rocky Alpine cliffs dusted by a freshly fallen powder snow and bathed in green moonlight."

More that's ahead: The Miami Seaquarium people are trying to keep alive and display to the public deep-dwelling fish, a thing that has been difficult or impossible. They are succeeding with silk snappers and black snappers, from 500- to 1,000-foot depths in the Gulf Stream, and with groupers, scorpion fish, Pensacola red snappers, sootfin snappers, and vermilion snappers, all from a depth of 200 feet or less.

Men will observe the depths and bottom while living in towns or homes that they may hollow out of the rock that forms the bottom of the sea itself. There will be exits from them so men can explore the bottom. The first city under the sea floor, for 50 men, Project Rock Site, is being built by the Navy in tunnels 70 to 700 feet beneath the sea floor near San Clemente Island, off California. Men are living in the sea for longer and longer periods both in Jacques-Yves Cousteau's Conshelf experiments and in the United States Navy's Sealabs. Scott Carpenter, 43 years old, stayed 30 days at 205 feet in Sealab II. Eventually the Sealab program will keep men 90 days at 850 feet.

A manned undersea station is possible atop a seamount, says Dr. Robert E. Burns of the University of Washington-ESSA research center, located in Seattle. Men would live atop Cobb Seamount, which rises in the Pacific, 300 miles west of Grays Harbor, Washington, from a depth of 10,000 feet to a point only 120 feet beneath the surface.

Work of all kinds will be simpler in the future in the depths or on the bottom. Men may have a domestic animal to help: The Navy is training porpoises to carry tools to divers and find lost divers. To learn porpoise behavior, Kenneth Norris has built his own one-man submersible to be towed behind ships and let him watch wild porpoises. He calls it his seasick machine. But it helps him see porpoises.

Oil wells on the bottom will be easier to drill because of electronic systems (Honeywell has one) that keep a drill ship in position over a well. Wells will be drilled in deeper water.

Divers will work in deeper water. In mid-August, 1967, divers Arthur Pachette and Glen Taylor for Esso Production Research Company of Houston and Ocean Systems set another diving record. Off Grand Isle, Louisiana, they dived to 636 feet and worked there. They returned to a helium-oxygen atmosphere in a pressure chamber on a surface ship, dived twice more to 636 feet, and altogether worked on the bottom six hours and remained under pressure equivalent to that of 636 feet of water for more than 48 hours—the longest time yet for men's bodies under that pressure. It was also the longest time men have breathed the helium-oxygen atmosphere required at the 636-foot level. When Pachette and Taylor returned to the deck chamber for the third time, they were gradually decompressed to normal surface pressure. The process took six days. Chet Smith, president of Ocean Systems, called the dive "an important milestone in extending man's ability to live and work efficiently in the sea."

Aboard *Deep Diver*, in the Bahamas at the edge of the Tongue of the Ocean, one day in 1968, divers Roger Cook and Denny Breese pressurized themselves, then stepped out of the submarine onto the sea bottom 700 feet down—the deepest working lockout dive on record. The first individual divers to roam the ocean floor at this depth, they collected brittle stars, shrimp, algae, and samples of the gently sloping, hard sand bottom. They could see 25 to 50 feet in the quite dark water without lights. They ran into a ½- to ¾-knot current that they believe is an eddy of the Gulf Stream. They stayed out at 700 feet for 15 minutes. Ed Link was in charge of the project, the Smithsonian Institution was a sponsor; Dr. Joseph B. MacInnis was in attendance in charge of the divers' medical needs, John Barringer was director of the dive, and Ray Stuart, master diving specialist, helped.

There will be more beacons on the bottom. In 1963, a transponder (made by the Bendix Corporation), designed to last one year, was lowered 6,000 feet below the surface of the Pacific. In 1967, it was still operating—sending out sounds by which ships and submarines could check their positions. Off Hawaii, the Oceanic Foundation—established by Taylor A. (Tap) Pryor, 35; chairmaned by Dr. James H. Wakelin, Jr., a former Assistant Secretary of the Navy for Research and Development; with Ken Norris as vice-president—is setting up an entire oceanographic research center. Men will live just offshore at 70- to 200-foot depths, instruments will test the adjoining sea to 18,000 feet down, and porpoises will be trained with the help of Mrs. Pryor.

In the future, we will have more sophisticated equipment, and it will do spectacular things. An outstanding job was recently done by an electronic FISH, a package of instruments that is also a robot device used at great depths. What happened was this: A FISH was being towed off the coast of Baja California to map the ocean bottom. It broke loose from its towing cable and sank in nearly 10,000 feet of water. The Scripps Research Vessel *Thomas Washington* towed another FISH above the path of the first one. By matching ocean-bottom profiles—an almost unbelievable feat, according to *American Oceanography*—the first FISH was located. Continued *American Oceanography*: "Then, a sled was dragged across the path of the old broken cable on the bottom. Delicate instruments indicated when the first FISH had been hooked and nine anxious hours were spent raising the package the mile and a half to the surface. This whole event was a remarkable recovery exercise. If you don't believe it, ask a flounder fisherman."

West Germany's TOURS (*T*ourist *O*bservation and *U*nderwater *R*esearch *S*ubmarines) will accommodate five or six men at depths to 1,000 feet. But the deepest underseas home yet, designed to house five scientists for 30 days at a depth of 6,000 feet, is being developed by General Dynamics for the United States Naval Civil Engineering Laboratory. It will have viewports to permit visual observation of the depths. North American Rockwell has a Navy contract to study the feasibility of habitats for as many as 1,000 men, also at 6,000 feet.

The world's first underwater museum will tell the story of the development of undersea frontiers. At Philadelphia, half a block from the Liberty Bell, an underwater museum opened in 1968. The public may visit it any day in the week. It is part of the Philadelphia Maritime Museum. Models and pictures of *Trieste I, Alvin, Deep Diver, Star II, Star III, Asherah,* and *Aluminaut* are shown. The museum even exhibits General Dynamics' *Star I*. The evolution of the submarine is shown, along with a model of Alexander the Great's glass diving bell. A popular exhibit is a beautiful gold chain and whistle, recovered by divers off Cape Kennedy, Florida—proof that some lost treasure from sunken treasure ships can be recovered. "Our new museum," says J. Wells Henderson, president of the Philadelphia Maritime Museum, "points out some of the complications involved in putting man underwater, but it also points out man's persistence. Humanity needs the fruits of the sea.

We are so convinced of the importance of the world oceans to mankind that we have devoted our underwater museum to the activities of this new breed of man—*homo aquaticus*—underwaterman."

So eager was the United States to get underway on the biggest exploration job on earth—that of the oceans—that by 1968 there are 15 oceanographic associations; there are 60 schools, universities, and institutions offering courses in oceanography; 110 federal government agencies, labs, and offices concerned with the oceans, and 725 companies offering ocean products and services. One company alone has 2,000 people in its undersea department. "When you first begin to grasp what this multi-billion dollar industry is becoming," said the December, 1967, *American Oceanography*, "you next have to ask what the oceans have to offer. The answer is simple—*our future.*"

"The history of mankind has always been closely associated with the sea," says Harold Bernstein. "Throughout his more than 5,000 years of history, man has instinctively struggled to explore and exploit the ocean environment surrounding and separating the world's great land masses. . . . For the ancients of Mesopotamia to the civilizations of the Nile, the Mediterranean, and the great Atlantic and Pacific oceans, no appreciable society has existed without access to water and used that water in commerce, communications and defense . . .

"It was the development of maritime technology which enabled Columbus, Magellan, Cabot, Balboa, Drake, and others to explore the New World. Trans-Atlantic trade fostered the rapid growth of the American colonies and, subsequently, gave birth to a new nation." Ever since, the sea has played a vital part in United States history. But men have largely used only the surface of the sea: only the top, the epidermis. Now men in their wonderful new deep-diving machines are going into what is called "innerspace"—the 330 million cubic miles of the ocean's depths. "Man's history—for more than 5,000 years," says Mr. Bernstein, "has been limited to the surface or near-surface of the sea. Now, a whole new history will be written of man's development with the ability to use the 98 percent of the sea not available to him today."

"One thing is certain," a paper by Lockheed's J. G. Wenzel and W. M. Helvey says, "and that is that man is not to be denied the wealth, adventure, and technical challenges of the ocean depths."

"We cross the oceans as routine," says Allyn Vine. "We are just now beginning to get to the bottom as routinely. My generation was brought up to think of the ocean as deep. My children's generation will think of it as shallow—that is, as accessible."

"We looked at this mysterious sea," Jules Verne wrote 100 years ago, "whose great depths had up to this time been inaccessible to the eye of man." For men to explore the depths was, 100 years ago, not fact—but a dream. Now at last men are looking at the depths. Now at last they are exploring the one area on the globe they never could reach before: the undersea frontiers.

Bibliography

BOOKS

ALLEE, W. C. and SCHMIDT, KARL P. *Ecological Animal Geography*. New York: John Wiley & Sons, Inc., 1951.

ARMSTRONG, E. F., and MIALL, L. M. *Raw Materials from the Sea*. New York: Chemical Publishing Co., Inc., 1946.

ARNOV, BORIS, JR. *Oceans of the World*. Indianapolis: The Bobbs-Merrill Co., Inc., 1962.

ARX, WILLIAM S. VON. *Proceedings of the Symposium on Aspects of Deep-Sea Research*. Washington, D.C.: National Academy of Sciences-National Research Council, 1957.

BAKER, B. B., JR., DEEBEL, W. R., GEISENDERFER, R. D. *Glossary of Oceanographic Terms*. Washington, D.C.: U.S. Naval Oceanographic Office, 2nd ed., 1966.

BEEBE, WILLIAM. *Half Mile Down*. New York: Harcourt, Brace & Co., 1934.

BERRILL, N. J. *The Life of the Ocean*. New York: McGraw-Hill Book Co., Inc., 1966.

BRELAND, OSMOND P. *Animal Life and Lore*. New York: Harper & Row, 1963.

BRUUN, ANTON FREDERIC, GREVE, SVEND B., MIELCHE, HAKON, SPARCK, HAKON R. G. *The Galathea Deep Sea Expedition, 1950-1952*. Trans. by Reginald Spink. London: Allen & Unwin, 1956.

BUCHSBAUM, RALPH. *Animals Without Backbones*. Chicago and London: The University of Chicago Press, 12th impression, 1965.

223

BUCHSBAUM, RALPH, and MILNE, LORUS J. *The Lower Animals, the Living Invertebrates of the World*. New York: Doubleday & Co., Inc., 1960.

BUREAU OF COMMERCIAL FISHERIES. *The Fisheries of North America*. Washington, D.C.: Circular 250, September, 1966.

CALVERT, JAMES. *Surface at the Pole (The extraordinary voyages of the USS SKATE)*. New York: McGraw-Hill Book Co., Inc., 1960.

CARRINGTON, RICHARD. *A Biography of the Sea*. New York: Basic Books, Inc., 1960.

CARSON, RACHEL L. *The Sea Around Us*. New York: Oxford University Press; soft-cover edition by Mentor Books, 1950.

CHALLENGER, H. M. S. *Challenger Reports*. Reprints available from Johnson Reprint Corp. New York, N.Y.

CLARKE, ARTHUR C. *The Challenge of the Sea*. New York: Holt, Rinehart & Winston, Inc., 1960; soft-cover edition by Dell Publishing Co., Inc., New York, 1966.

COUSTEAU, JACQUES-YVES, and DUGAN, JAMES. *The Living Sea*. New York: Harper & Row, 1963.

COUSTEAU, JACQUES-YVES. *The Silent World*. Harper & Row: soft-cover edition by Pocket Books, Inc., New York, 1953.

———. *World Without Sun*. New York: Harper & Row, 1965.

COWEN, ROBERT C. *Frontiers of the Sea*. New York: Doubleday & Co., Inc., 1960.

CROMIE, WILLIAM J. *Exploring the Secrets of the Sea*. Englewood Cliffs, N.J.: Prentice-Hall, Inc., 1962.

DEACON, G. E. R., ed. *Seas, Maps and Men*. New York: Doubleday & Co., Inc., 1962.

DUGAN, JAMES. *Man Under the Sea*. New York: Harper & Bros., 1956.

ENGEL, LEONARD, and the Editors of *Life*. *The Sea*. New York: Time, Inc., 1961.

ERICSON, DAVID B., and WOLLIN, GOESTA. *The Deep and the Past*. New York: Alfred A. Knopf, 1964.

GASKELL, T. F. *Under the Deep Oceans*. New York: W. W. Norton & Co., Inc., 1960.

GILG, JOSEPH G., and McCONNELL, JAMES J., JR. *Non-Existent Seamounts—A Case Study*. Naval Oceanographic Office, September, 1966.

GRAY, WILLIAM B. *Creatures of the Sea*. New York: Wilfred Funk, Inc., 1960.

GUNTHER, KLAUS, and DECKERT, KURT. *Creatures of the Deep Sea*. New York: Charles Scribner's Sons, 1956.

HARDY, SIR ALISTER. *The Open Sea*. Boston: Houghton Mifflin Co., 1956.

HEGNER, ROBERT W., and STILES, KARL A. *College Zoology*. New York: The Macmillan Co., 6th ed., 1951.

HILL, M. N., ed. *The Sea*. New York: John Wiley & Sons, Inc., Vol. 1, 1962; Vol. 2, 1963; Vol. 3, 1963.

HOUOT, GEORGES, and WILLM, PIERRE. *2000 Fathoms Down*. New York: E. P. Dutton & Co., Inc., 1955.

IDYLL, C. P. *Abyss: The Deep Sea and the Creatures that Live in It*. New York: Thomas Y. Crowell Co., 1964.

INTERAGENCY COMMITTEE ON OCEANOGRAPHY. *National Oceanographic Program*. Washington, D.C.: Federal Council for Science and Technology, 1967.

KING, C. A. M. *Introduction to Oceanography*. New York: McGraw-Hill Book Co., Inc., 1963.

LAFAYETTE COLLEGE. *Ocean Science and Technology*. Easton, Pennsylvania, pamphlet.

LANE, FRANK W. *Kingdom of the Octopus*. London: Jarrolds, 1957.

LARSON, HOWARD E. *A History of Self-Contained Diving and Underwater Swimming*. Washington, D.C.: National Academy of Sciences-National Research Council, 1959.

LONG, CAPTAIN E. JOHN. *New Worlds of Oceanography*. New York: Pyramid Publications, 1965.

MARSHALL, N. B. *Aspects of Deep Sea Biology*. London: Hutchinson and Co., Ltd., 1954.

MENARD, H. W. *Marine Geology of the Pacific*. New York: McGraw-Hill Book Co., Inc., 1964.

MERO, JOHN L. *The Mineral Resources of the Sea*. New York: American Elsevier Publishing Co., Inc., 1964.

MILLER, ROBERT C. *The Sea*. New York: Random House, 1966.

MURRAY, SIR JOHN. *The Ocean*. New York: Henry Holt & Co., undated.

MURRAY, SIR JOHN, and HJORT, JOHAN. *The Depths of the Ocean*. London: Macmillan & Co., Ltd., 1912.

NATIONAL ASSOCIATION OF MANUFACTURERS. *New Wealth from the Seas*. New York, 1966.

NORMAN, J. R., and FRASER, F. C. *Giant Fishes, Whales and Dolphins*. New York: W. W. Norton, 1938.

OMMANNEY, F. D., and the Editors of *Life*. *The Fishes*. New York: Time, Inc., 1963.

PHILLIPS, CRAIG. *The Captive Sea*. New York: Chilton Co., 1964.

PICCARD, JACQUES, and DIETZ, ROBERT S. *Seven Miles Down*. New York: G. P. Putnam's Sons, 1961.

RITCHIE, GEORGE STEPHEN. *"Challenger:" The Life of a Survey Ship.* New York: Abelard-Schuman Ltd., 1958.

SCHMITT, WALDO L. *Crustaceans.* Ann Arbor: The University of Michigan Press, 1965.

SCHULTZ, LEONARD P., and others. *Wondrous World of Fishes.* Washington, D.C.: National Geographic Society, 1965.

SEARS, MARY, ed. *Progress in Oceanography.* New York: The Macmillan Co., 1964.

SILVERBERG, ROBERT. *The World of the Ocean Depths.* New York: Meredith Press, 1968.

SMITH, J. L. B. *The Search Beneath the Sea.* New York: Henry Holt & Co., 1956

SOULE, GARDNER. *The Ocean Adventure.* New York: Meredith Press/Appleton-Century, 1966.

STENUIT, ROBERT. *The Deepest Days.* New York: Coward-McCann, Inc., 1966.

STEPHENS, WILLIAM M. *Science Beneath the Sea.* New York: G. P. Putnam's Sons, 1966.

STEWART, HARRIS B. *The Global Sea.* Princeton, N.J.: D. Van Nostrand Co., Inc., 1963.

STILES, NEWELL T. *Mass Property Relationships of Sediments from the Hatteras Abyssal Plain.* Washington, D.C.: Naval Oceanographic Office, February, 1967.

SVERDRUP, H. U., JOHNSON, MARTIN W., FLEMING, RICHARD H. *The Oceans.* New York: Prentice-Hall, Inc., 1942.

TAILLIEZ, PHILIPPE. *To Hidden Depths.* New York: E. P. Dutton & Co., Inc., 1954.

TEXAS, UNIVERSITY OF. *Marine Sciences—Industrial Potentials.* Austin, Texas, 1967.

TOLSTOY, IVAN. *Submarine Topography in the North Atlantic.* Bulletin of the Geological Society of America, May, 1951.

TROEBST, CORD-CHRISTIAN. *Conquest of the Sea.* New York: Harper & Row, 1962.

UNESCO. *Oceans, Science, and Men.* 1964.

U.S. BUREAU OF COMMERCIAL FISHERIES, HAWAII AREA BIOLOGICAL LABORATORY, HONOLULU, HAWAII. *Progress in 1962-63. Progress in 1961-62. Progress in 1960. Past (1949-1958), Present (1959), Future 1960—). Fish Schools and Bird Flocks in Central Pacific Ocean, 1950-61.*

U.S. NATIONAL COUNCIL ON MARINE RESOURCES. *United States Activities in Spacecraft Oceanography.* Washington, D.C., 1967.

U.S. NAVAL OCEANOGRAPHIC OFFICE. *Catalog of Oceanographic Technical Reports and Special Publications.* Washington, D.C., 1967.

U.S. NAVAL OCEANOGRAPHIC OFFICE. *Oceanography '66 Annual Report.* Washington, D.C., 1966.

U.S. NAVY. *Aircraft Salvage Operation Mediterranean* (The H-Bomb Recovery). Washington, D. C., 1967.

U.S. NAVY ELECTRONICS LABORATORY. *NEL Deep Submergence Log No. 1, for period 6 June through 2 July 1966.* San Diego, California, August, 1966.

U.S. NAVY ELECTRONICS LABORATORY. *NEL Deep Submergence Log No. 2, for period 3 July through 3 September 1966.* San Diego, California, October, 1966.

U.S. NAVY ELECTRONICS LABORATORY. *NEL Deep Submergence Log No. 3, for period 4 September through 23 December 1966.* San Diego, California, February, 1967.

U.S. NAVY, OFFICE OF NAVAL RESEARCH. *Project Sealab Report.* Washington, D.C., 1967.

U.S. WHITE HOUSE. *Effective Use of the Sea: Report of the Panel on Oceanography, President's Science Advisory Committee.* Washington, D.C., June, 1966.

U.S. WHITE HOUSE. *Marine Science Affairs: The First Report of the President to the Congress on Marine Resources and Engineering Development.* Washington, D.C., February, 1967.

VERRILL, A. HYATT. *The Ocean and Its Mysteries.* New York: Duffield & Co., 1917.

VILLIERS, ALAN. *Men, Ships, and the Sea.* Washington, D.C.: National Geographic Society, 1963.

WALFORD, LIONEL A. *Living Resources of the Sea.* New York: The Ronald Press Co., 1958.

WOODS HOLE OCEANOGRAPHIC INSTITUTION. *Alvin Dives on the Continental Margin off the Southeastern United States July 2-13, 1967.* Woods Hole, Massachusetts, December, 1967. Unpublished manuscript.

WOODS HOLE OCEANOGRAPHIC INSTITUTION. *Deep Submergence Research Conducted During the Period 1 January through 31 December 1965.* Woods Hole, Massachusetts, June, 1966. Unpublished manuscript.

WOODS HOLE OCEANOGRAPHIC INSTITUTION. *Deep Submergence Research Conducted During the Period 1 January through 31 December 1966.* Woods Hole, Massachusetts, April, 1967. Unpublished manuscript.

ARTICLES

BALDWIN, HANSON W. "New Submarines Will Explore the Last Frontier," *New York Times,* July 26, 1965.

BALDWIN, HANSON W. "Undersea Research and Exploration Growing Rapidly Throughout the World," *New York Times*, July 25, 1965.

BARHAM, DR. ERIC. "Deep Scattering Layer Migration and Composition: Observations from a Diving Saucer." *Science*, Vol. 151, March 18, 1966.

CLEARY, JOHN. "Oceans Still Unexploited While Man Tests Space," *Hartford* (Conn.) *Times*, March 25, 1965.

————. "Conquest of the Seas Called as Valuable as Moon Venture," *New York World-Telegram & Sun*, December 3, 1965.

CROMIE, WILLIAM J. " 'Doc' The story of William Maurice Ewing," *Rice University Review*, Fall/Winter, 1967.

DUGGAN, DENNIS. "Companies Hunt Untapped Riches Beneath the Sea," *New York Herald Tribune*, October 25, 1964.

ELIA, CHARLES. "From Oil Rig to Trawler Fleet, Oceanics Explores New World," *New York World-Telegram & Sun*, June 6, 1964.

HULL, E. W. SEABROOK. "Those Remarkable Little Work Boats" (deep research submarines), *Geo Marine Technology*, Intel, Inc., Washington, D.C., May, 1967.

"OCEANOLOGY" (on deep research submarines) *Time*, January 19, 1968.

SOULE, GARDNER. "In Quest of the Key to Davy Jones' Locker," *Elks Magazine*, Benevolent and Protective Order of Elks, August, 1965.

SOULE, GARDNER, and ARMAGNAC, ALDEN P. "The Fabulous Machines That Recovered Our H-Bomb," *Popular Science*, New York, June, 1966.

VINE, ALLYN. "Tools for Ocean Research," *International Science and Technology*, New York, Conover-Mast Publications, December, 1965; see also issue of March, 1965.

WILLATT, NORRIS. "Wealth from the Sea? Venturesome Companies Are Taking the Plunge into Oceanography," *Barron's National Business & Financial Weekly*, Chicopee, Mass., Dow Jones & Co., Inc. May 17, 1965.

WUST, GEORG. "The Major Deep-Sea Expeditions and Research Vessels 1873-1960." Reprinted from *Progress in Oceanography*, Vol. 2, Pergamon Press, London, New York, 1964.

MAGAZINES

All Hands. The Bureau of Naval Personnel, Washington, D.C., monthly.

American Oceanography. American Society for Oceanography, Houston, Texas, newsletter.

The Bulletin. U.S. Naval Oceanographic Office, Washington, D.C., bi-weekly.

Columbia University News Bulletin (No. 8219 for March 11, 1960), New York City.

Gulf Review. Gulf Universities Research Corporation, Texas, newsletter.

The Humble Way. Humble Oil & Refining Company, Houston, Texas, quarterly.

Hydrogram. Data Publications, Washington, D.C., newsletter.

Journal of Hydronautics. American Institute of Aeronautics and Astronautics Inc., quarterly.

Journal of Ocean Technology. The Marine Technology Society, Washington, D.C., quarterly.

Life. Special issues on the oceans, February 9, 1953; December 21, 1962.

MTS Memo. Marine Technology Society, Washington, D.C., newsletter.

Maritimes. Kingston, R.I. University of Rhode Island Graduate School of Oceanography, quarterly.

National Fisherman. Camden, Maine. Russell W. Brace, publisher, monthly.

Naval Institute Proceedings. Annapolis, Maryland, U.S. Naval Institute, monthly.

Naval Research Reviews. U.S. Navy Office of Naval Research, Washington, D.C., monthly.

Ocean Science News. Nautilus Press, Inc., Washington, D.C., weekly newsletter.

Oceanography. Mardee Enterprises, Inc., New York, newsletter.

Oceanology International. Industrial Research, Inc., Beverly Shores, Indiana.

Oceanus. The Woods Hole Oceanographic Institution, Woods Hole, Massachusetts, quarterly.

Petroleum Today. The American Petroleum Institute, New York, Summer 1967.

Science. American Association for the Advancement of Science, Washington, D.C., December 2, 1966.

Sea Frontiers. International Oceanographic Foundation, Miami, Florida, six times a year.

Sea Secrets. International Oceanographic Foundation, Miami, Florida, monthly.

Underwater Naturalist. Highlands, N.J. American Littoral Society, Sandy Hook Marine Laboratory.

Index

A

Abyss, 182
Acorn worm, tracks of, 196
Adams, Rear Admiral K. T.,
    134
Adams, Mike, 165, 174
Aegean Sea, explorations in,
    32
Air Force Strategic Air Com-
    mand, 165
Airplane, F6F, preserved by
    sea, 159, 160
Alaska earthquake, Good Fri-
    day (1964), 158, 159
Albany, 173
Aleutian Islands, 133-134
Aleutian Trench, 193
Alexander the Great, 119-120,
    124, 219
  diving bell, model of, 219
  monster, 120, 124
Alexander's Acres, 137-138

Algae, 218
Aluminaut, 14-21, 31, 34, 37,
    43-51, 61, 64, 88, 90, 104,
    109, 119, 140, 143, 159,
    179, 201-207, 213, 219
  deepest dive, 50
  in H-bomb hunt, 169, 170,
    174
  record research dive, 91
Aluminum, 152
Alvin, 31, 34, 49, 64, 84-90,
    104, 137, 138, 140-149,
    159, 179, 213, 215, 216,
    219
  in H-bomb hunt, 167, 168,
    169, 170, 171, 172, 174
  log of Dive 200, 140-144
  trip report of Dive 201, 145,
    146
Amberjack, 33, 86
American Association for the
    Advancement of Science,
    198

American Geological Institute, 215
Geotimes, 215
American Museum of Natural History, 33, 182
American Oceanography, quoted, 219, 220
American Scientist, 132, 133, 138
American Scout, 131 ff
  seamount, 132 ff
American Submarine Company, 31-32
Amersub 300, 31
Amersub 600, 31
Amorphous silica, 206
Amos, Tony, 196
Amphipods, deep-dwelling, 154
Andaman Islands, 130
Anderson, William G., 47
Andrea Doria, 174
Anhydrite, 206
Animal Life and Lore, 58
Animals
  deepest dwelling, 153-154
  unknown, 23
  see also Monster; Sea serpent
Antarctic, sea cucumbers in, 129
Anton Bruun, 62, 64
Apollo spaceship, 107, 114, 202
Aquarium
  National, 18
  Niagara Falls, 39
Archaeology, submarine in, 32
Archimede, 197
Arctic Ocean, sea cucumbers in, 129

Arctic Ocean Range, 193
Arnov, Boris, Jr., 58
Ascension Island, 117
Asherah, 32, 33, 69, 219
Astro Marine, 68
Atlantic Fleet Weapons Range, Navy, 49
Atlantic Ocean
  bathyscaphe dives, 196-197
  squid, 213-214
  undersea current, 152-153
Atlantic Oceanographic Laboratories (ESSA), 126
Atlantic Undersea Test and Evaluation Center (AUTEC), 86
  Autec I, 34
  Autec II, 34
Atlantis (mythical city), 64
Atlantis, 190, 205
Atlantis II, 134, 138, 206
Auguste Piccard, 98-99
Austin, Dr. Thomas S., 152, 153
Azores Islands, 116, 117

B

Bache, Alexander Dallas, 93
Backus, Dr. Richard H., 38, 138
Bacteria, 70
Bahama Banks, 202
Bahama Escarpment, 203
Bahamas, 40-41, 49, 85
  record fish caught off, 86
Bahamas Ministry of Tourism, 85

Barbee, Lieutenant Commander, 127
Barham, Dr. Eric, 136, 137
Barkich, Joe, 171
Barnacles, 211
Barracuda, 59
    attack squid, 214
Barringer, John L., Jr., 167, 168, 218
Barton, Otis, 94, 174
Basalt slopes, 186
    see also Canyons, undersea
Bass-like fish, 145
Basserga, Horacio, 105, 106
Bassogigas (brotulid), 55
Bathyscaphe, 24, 49, 87, 94, 102, 152, 195
    diving in Atlantic, 197
    see also Archimede;
        F.N.R.S. 3; Trieste;
        Trieste II
Bathysphere, 94, 174
Bauxite, 152
Beach, Captain Edward L., 92
Beagles, John, 213
Beaver Mark IV, 34
Beebe, William, 94, 129, 174
Belyaev, Russian scientist, 154
Ben Franklin (PX-15), 91-99
Bendix Corporation, 160, 218
Bennett, Dr. Harry, 47
Benthos Company, 121
Benthosaurus (tripod fish), 87, 151-152
Bering Sea, 133
Bermuda
    sea fans off, 118, 119
Bernstein, Harold, 122, 178, 220

Berryhill, Dr. Henry L., Jr., 157
Biography of the Sea, A, 183, 210
Biological Laboratory, Bureau of Commercial Fisheries, 32-33
Bivalves, 154
Black sands, 156
Blackfish, dead, 55
Blake Plateau, 15-17, 83, 89, 140-147, 155, 156
    core hole drilled, 156
Bland, Edward, 159
Blennies, 55
Boeing, 111
Bonita, 100
Bottom of the sea
    black, 14 ff
    brownish gray, 23
    flat, 15
    greenish gray, 27
    lifeless, 52 ff
    living on, *see* Living on the bottom of sea
    oil walls, 83, 217
    olive gray, 216
    rose-colored, 154-155
Boulenger, E. G., 39
Bourne, Donald W., 196
Bradley, Bob, 53, 55, 56, 214
Breathing in deep-diving sub, 107
Breese, Dennison K., 49, 170, 218
Breland, Osmond P., 58
Briggs, Edward, 105
Brimberg, Fred, 173
Bristlemouth (fish), 38

Brittle stars, 22, 102, 113, 129, 146, 213, 218
  lack of in lifeless depths, 53, 54
Brogan, Tom W., 173
Bromine from seawater, 210, 211
Brooks, Dr. Kelly, 19, 46
Brotulid, 55
Brown, Captain Edward B., 117, 128
Bryozoans, 146
Buchsbaum, Ralph, 37
Bugs, sea, 147
Bullis, Harvey, 47
Burchtide, 54, 111 ff
Bureau of Commercial Fisheries, United States, 32, 33, 96 ff, 152, 209, 211
Bureau of Sport Fisheries and Wildlife, 59, 60
Burma, undersea mountains, 118
Burns, Dr. Robert E., 217
Busby, R. Frank, 47, 49
Butterfly fish, 158

C

Cable, telephone, inspection of, 29, 30
Caiman, 100
Calcium from seawater, 210
Calvert, Rear Admiral James, 97
Cambridge University, 196
Camera, deep-sea, 17, 53, 59, 60, 62, 114, 195, 196

Camera, deep-sea—*cont.*
  Edgerton, 143
  Lamont, 63
  movie, 143
  TV, 97, 98, 203
Campbell, Bob, 23, 25
Canary, Robert H., 47-49
  in H-bomb hunt, 170
Canyons, undersea, 88-89, 150-151, 183, 186, 192, 197
  see also Cliffs, undersea; Mountains, undersea; Volcanoes, undersea
Cape Hatteras, 16, 137, 147-148
Cape Johnson, 126
Carpenter, Malcolm Scott, 85, 217
Carr, Archie, 117
Carrington, Richard, 183, 210
Carthage, exploration site, 203
Cascade, 171
Casey, James D., 165
Cave in sea bottom, 151
Chain, 204-206
Chalk layer, from sea bottom, 193-194
Challenger Deep, 94-95
Challenger expedition, 118, 196
Chang, Randolph K. C., 96
Chaunax (golden pouched fish), 145
Chimaeri collei (ratfish), 113
China Lake (Calif.)
  Naval Ordnance Test Station, 165, 184
  Naval Weapons Center, 122, 165
Church, Ron, 110 ff, 214-215
City, under sea, project, 216

Civil Engineering Laboratory, Naval, 219
Clams, 71, 72
Cliffs, undersea, 32-33, 41, 88-89, 151, 155 ff, 186, 216
  see also Canyons, undersea; Mountains, undersea
Cobb Seamount, 130, 217
Collision of heavenly bodies, 194
Colors in sea, 216
  under ultraviolet light, 186, 187
  see also Bottom of sea
Columbia University, 17, 78, 118, 155, 156, 189 ff
Columbia University Club, 58
Columns, on sea bottom, 62-65
Conger, 30
Conshelf, 217
Conshelf II, 204
Continental Can Pier, 191
Continental drift theory, 193, 199
Continental rise, 155
Continental shelf, 156, 200
  core hole drilled, 156
Continental slope, 147, 156, 181-188
  core hole drilled, 156
Cook, Roger, 218
Cooke, Rockne F., 173
Cooney, Jim, 13-20, 49, 50-51, 170, 215
Copepods, 51
Copper, 204, 205, 207
Coral, 128, 130, 142, 144
  alcyonarian, 146
  deep-water, 146

Coral—*cont.*
  gorgonian, 186
  red, 33
Coral fish, 39
Core-hole drilling, 156
Core samples, 156, 205
Corer, free, 121
Corning Glass Works, 119 ff
Cousteau, Jacques-Yves, 31, 33, 34, 35, 58, 96, 110, 136, 150, 152, 153, 183, 204, 217
  see also Diving saucer
Cowen, Robert C., 181, 182
Crabs, 18, 40, 66, 67, 68, 142, 145, 183, 187
  biggest, 182
  lack of in lifeless depths, 52, 53
  large, 39
  spider, 146, 182
Criger, Harold, 25
Crinoids (sea lilies), 128-129, 143, 183, 214
Cromwell, Townsend, 153
Cromwell Current, 153
Cronkite, Walter, 80-81, 183, 184
Cubmarine, 31
  PC3B, in H-bomb hunt, 164, 165, 166, 167, 174
Current meters, recovery of, 47-49
Currents
  Blake Plateau, 141-142
  Cromwell Current, 153
  deep, 155, 156
  importance of, 92
  in Pacific, 184
  turbidity, 182, 194, 196

CURV, in H-bomb recovery, 171-173
Cyclothone (bristlemouth), 38

D

Dale, Barrie, 159, 160
Dana, James D., 33
David Taylor Model Basin, 119
Dead Sea, saline content, 206
Deaton, Don, 85, 86
Deep Diver, 31, 75-77, 81-83, 213, 218, 219
Deep Jeep, 31, 104, 122, 181, 184-188
  in H-bomb recovery, 165
Deep-ocean simulator, 104 ff
Deep Quest, 21-28, 31, 49, 64, 82, 88, 102, 103-109, 178, 213
Deep scattering layer, 136 ff, 147, 148
Deep Submergence Systems Project, Navy, 122, 175, 177-179
Deep View, 122
Deepstar 2000, 34
Deepstar 4000, 14, 22, 31, 33, 52-58, 61, 104, 110-115, 137, 183, 184, 213, 214, 215
Deepstar 20,000, 35, 175
Deepstar monster, 22, 57 ff
DeHart, Dr. Robert C., 105
Delauze, Dr. Henri, 197
Dendrophyllia (deep-water coral), 146
Depth perception, lack of, 184

Depths, lifeless, 52-56
Deuterium, 211
Diamonds, 33, 157
Dietrich, G., 206
Diffenderfer, J. H., 105
Dill, Dr. Robert F., 101, 215
Dippy, R. N., 105
Discoverer, 17
Discovery, 206
Dive
  submarine, price of, 202, 203
  working lockout, 218
Diver
  equipment of, 128
  problems of, 76
Dives, record
  Aluminaut's, 21, 48 ff
  Alvin's, 84 ff
  Deep Quest's, 21 ff
  longest deep, 78
  Trieste's, 94-95, 100
  working lockout, 218
Diving, history of, 120
Diving saucer, 33, 34, 58, 96, 101, 110, 136, 150, 151, 183, 204, 215
  see also Cousteau
Dogfish (shark), 142, 146
Dolphin, fish, 86, 97
Dolphin (555), 35
DOWB (Deep Ocean Work Boat), 31
Drugs from sea, 210-211
D/RV's (deep research vehicles), 13
DSRV (Deep Submergence Rescue Vehicle), 175-179
  DSRV-1, 175-178
Dugong, 19

Duke University, 62, 155, 156, 157
Dust in sea, 183
Dust storm beneath sea, 160

E

Earthquake, Alaska, Good Friday (1964), 158, 159
Eastward, 155
Echinoderms, 129
Echinoids, 143
Echo sounder, 132, 135, 136, 138
Edgerton camera, 143
Eel-like fish, 148
Eels, 18
    deep-sea, 39, 145
    moray, 158
    with more than one heart, 183, 184
Eisenhower, Dwight D., 191
Ela, D. K., 215
Elisha Kane, 135
Eltanin, 195
Entemedor, 30
Enteropneust (acorn worm), 196
Environmental Science Services Administration (ESSA)
    Atlantic Oceanographic Laboratories, 126
    Institute of Oceanography, 127
    Land and Sea Interaction Laboratory, 17
    University of Washington research center, 217

Epsom salts from sea, 211
Ericson, David B., 198, 199
ESSA research center, 217
Esso Norway, Incorporated, 83
Esso Production Research Company, 217
Euphausiids, 26, 137
Ever-Changing Sea, The, 198
Ewing, John, 195
Ewing, Dr. William Maurice, 78, 118, 189-200
Explorers of the Sea, 119, 120

F

F-4, 179
F.N.R.S. 3, 152, 153
Falco, Albert, 215
Feldman, Samuel, 180
Feray, Dr. Dan E., 47
Fischer, Raymond C., 173
Fish
    abyssal, 195
    cleaners, 158
    clouds of, 96
    commonest, 38
    at greatest depths, 95
    monster, *see* Monster
    noise of, 95
    record, 58-59, 86
    school of, 94
    triangular, 152
    tripod (Benthosaurus), 151-152
    unknown, *see* Monster
FISH, electronic, 218, 219
Fiske, Samuel L., 73

Flatfish, 148, 186
  at greatest depths, 95
Flea-like organisms, 146
Floors of ocean in motion, 198
Florida, 18, 19, 119
  deep current off, 155
  see also Miami Seaquarium
Florida, University of, 19, 46
Florida State University, 62, 154
Foraminifera, 154, 193-194
Forman, Willis, R., 122, 184, 185, 188
  in H-bomb hunt, 165
Fort Snelling, 167, 168
Franklin, Benjamin, 93
Fraser, F. C., 58
Free corer, 121
Frontiers of the Sea, 181-182
Fye, Dr. Paul M., 206, 207

G

Gagarin, Yuri A., 85
Galanopoulos, Professor A. G., 64
Galathea, 55, 154
Galleon, 15th-century, 44, 45, 61, 159, 207
Galveston, Texas, 190
Gas wells, 155
Gastropods, lack of in lifeless depths, 53
Gemini (oil barge), 68, 73
Gemini spaceship, 107
General Dynamics, 14, 35, 219
  Electric Boat Division, 30, 34, 120

General Dynamics—*cont.*
  Underwater Development Engineering, 73
General Electric's Re-Entry Systems Department, 119
General Motors, 184
  AC Electronics Division, 31
General Precision Equipment Corporation, 164
Geo Marine Technology, 167
Geological Society of America, 190
Georgia-Florida, deep current off, 155
Geotimes, 215
Gerard, Robert D. (Sam), 156
Gereben, Istvan B., 173
Germany, West, deep-diving submarine, 219
Giant Fishes, Whales and Dolphins, 58
Gibraltar, Straits of, 204
Gilg, Joseph G., 132, 134, 135, 138
Gilliss, 134, 135
Giovanola
  Auguste Piccard, 98
  PX-15, 98
Glass, Bill, 194
Glass ceramic material, 119, 122
Glass house, 119 ff
Glass submarines, 122 ff
Glass under pressure, 121
Glauconite, 145, 156
Glenn, John, 85
Globigerina, 47-48, 141, 142, 144
Gobies, neon, 158

Goland, Martin, 105
Gold, 16, 204, 205, 207, 211
Gold-bearing sands, 157
Golden pouched fish, 145
Goldfish-like fish, 145
Gollwitzer, Robert L., 173
Good, Dale, 53, 55
Gooding, Reginald M., 96
Gorgonians (sea fans), 118, 143, 183, 214
Grand Banks, 203
    part of continental shelf, 200
Grant, Bruce, 17
Grapnel, in H-bomb recovery, 171, 172
Grauch, William F., 173
Gray, Captain Bill, 45, 97, 158
Great Barrier Reef, 129
    sea anemones on, 39
    sea cucumbers on, 129
Great Salt Lake, 206
Greenland shark, 60
Grouper, 79, 86, 142, 158, 216
Gruen, Henry M., 173
Grumman Aircraft Engineering Corporation, 82, 91, 95, 98
GSV-1, 82, 98
Guberlet, Muriel, 119
Guest, Rear Admiral William S., in H-bomb recovery, 163, 164, 172, 174
Guinness Book of World Records, quoted, 209
Gulf Stream, 15, 19, 71, 91-99, 141, 147, 203, 216
    eddy of, 218
    history of, 93
    importance of, 92
    speed of, 92

Gulf Universities Research Corporation (GURC), 35
Guppy, 34

H

H-bomb, search for,
    Adams, Mike, and, 165, 174
    Aluminaut and, 44, 48, 169, 170, 174
    Alvin and, 167, 168, 169, 170, 171, 172, 174
    Canary, Robert H., and, 170
    Cubmarine *PC3B* and, 164, 165, 166, 167, 174
    CURV and, 171-173
    Deep Jeep and, 165
    Forman, Willis R., and, 165
    Grapnel and, 171, 172
    Guest, Rear Admiral William S., and, 163, 164, 172, 174
    Hays, Dr. Earl E., and, 167
    Lindbergh, Jon Morrow, and, 164, 165, 174
    McCamis, Marvin J., and, 167, 168, 171, 172
    Markel, Art, and, 44, 169
    Mechanical arm, 170
    Minesweepers, 166
    Naval Oceanographic Office and, 164, 167
    Ocean Bottom Search Sonar and, 162 ff
    Ocean Systems, Incorporated and, 164, 167
    Palomares, Spain, 162 ff
    Pitts, Captain Ray M., 164
    Rainnie, William Ogg, Jr., and, 167, 171

H-bomb—*cont.*
  Scuba divers and, 173
  Serfass, Robert E., and, 169, 170
  Smith, Admiral A. C. (Chet), and, 164
  Stephan, Rear Admiral E. C., and, 164
  Task Force 65 and, 163 ff
  TV cameras, use of in, 171
  United States Sixth Fleet and, 163 ff
  Westinghouse Electric Corporation and, 167, 173
  Wilson, Valentine, and, 167, 168, 172
  Woods Hole Oceanographic Institution and, 167
Hagfish, 113
  with three hearts, 214
Hahn and Clay, Incorporated, 122
Harder, 134
Hardy, Sir Alister, 37
Hassler, Dr. Robert, 88
Hatchetfish, 18, 137, 145
Hatteras, Cape, 16, 137, 147-148
  and Gulf Stream, 93
Hawaii, University of, 33
Hays, Dr. Earl E., 167
Heavy hydrogen, 211
Heezen, Dr. Bruce C., 155, 193, 194, 196
Heinlein, Donald F., 173
Heirtzler, Dr. James R., 198
Helium, breathing gas, 78, 80, 217
Heller, Richard, 171

Helvey, W. M., 221
Henderson, J. Wells, 219
Henifin, Lieutenant Commander E. E., 180
Heron, Dr. S. Duncan, 156
Hess, Harry, 126
Hikino, 123
Hill, Robert G., 67-74, 160
Hiller, Melvin, 167, 173
Himalayas, 118, 182
Hole, Core, 156
Holland, John Philip, 43
Hollister, Charles, 155
Holothurians (sea cucumbers), 22, 102, 129, 145, 216
Homo aquaticus, 220
Honeywell, 217
Hornick, Clay, 159
Hot water, in Red Sea, 205-207
Houot, Commander Georges, 94, 102, 152, 153, 197
Hubbs, Carl, 60
Humble, 141, 149
Humble Oil & Refining Company, 156
Humphrey, Vice-President Hubert
  quoted, 211
Humuhumunukunukuapuaa, 97
Hunt, Dr. John M., 205
Hydrographer's Canyon, 159
Hydrographic Office, Naval, 132
Hydroid (jellyfish), 24, 55, 97-98, 142, 143, 146, 147
Hydronauts, 35, 179, 180
Hydrozoans, 22

I

Idyll, Dr. Clarence P., 18, 182
India, undersea mountains, 118
Indian Ocean
  explorations, 117, 127
  undercurrent, 153
Institute of Oceanography
  (ESSA), 127
Iodine from sea, 210-211
Iron, 156, 204, 207
  oxides, 205, 206
  sands, 157
Isaacs, Professor John D., 59,
  60, 61
Isopods
  biggest, 154
  deep-sea, 154, 157

J

Java, 117
Jawfish, 215
Jellyfish, 24, 55, 97-98, 142,
  143, 146, 147
Johns Hopkins University, 191
Johnson, Commander Phil, 184
JOIDES (Joint Oceanogra-
  phic Institution for Deep
  Earth Sampling), 156
Jolley, Jim, 165
Jones, Robert S., 173

K

K-3, 100
Kaye, Clifford A., 152

Kendall, T. Robert, 49
Kevin Moran, 78
Khune, Pete, 40
Kientzy, Raymond (Canoe),
  96
Klingel, Gilbert C., 129-130
Krill, 26, 137
Kunz, Herman (Bud), 171
Kurile-Kamchatka Trench,
  154

L

Lafayette College, 210
LaFond, Dr. Eugene C., 52-61
LaFond, Katherine, 54
Laing, Joseph, 173
Lamont, Thomas W., 191
Lamont camera, 63
Lamont Geological Observa-
  tory, 17, 118, 155, 189,
  191 ff
Land and Sea Interaction Lab-
  oratory (ESSA), 17
Lantern fish, 37-38, 136, 137,
  138, 147
  aboard *Star III*, 37, 38
  school of, 138
Larsen, Ensign Paul, 125, 127-
  130
Larson, Lieutenant Com-
  mander Wes, 177
Laughton, A. S., 118
Lehigh University, 190
Leonov, Alexei A., 85
Life, 81
Life of the Ocean, quoted, 39-
  40

Lifeless sea bottom, 52 ff
Limbaugh, Connie, 126
Lindbergh, Jon Morrow, 77-79, 80, 82
  in H-bomb hunt, 164, 165, 174
Link, Edwin Albert, 31, 77, 78, 79, 81, 82, 83, 86, 218
Link Aviation Trainers, 77
Lintz, Dr. George, 156
Little, Harold A., 170
Little Known Facts About the Submarine (booklet), quoted, 120
Litton Industries, 31, 85
Living on bottom of sea, 78 ff, 204, 216, 217, 218, 219
Lobsters, 30
  spiny, 33
Lockheed, 31, 82, 102, 103 ff, 221
  C-5A airplane, 176
  C-141 airplane, 176
  Missiles and Space Company, 22, 178
  Ocean Systems Organization, 25
  Sub-porter, 108, 109
Log
  Alvin's Dive, 140-144, 200
  Pioneer, 127, 128, 130
Loma sea valley, 213
Lombardi, Mary, 129
Long, Jack, 169
Lophelia (deep-water coral), 146
Louisiana State University, 47
Lovell, Otis W., 173
Lowell, John F., 170

Lower Animals, quoted, 37
Lulu, 89, 90, 141, 149
Luminescence, 72, 161
Lyon, Dr. Waldo, 97

M

McCamis, Marvin J., 84, 87 ff, 138, 140-149, 159, 160
  in H-bomb hunt, 167, 168, 171, 172
McCann rescue bell, 178
McConnell, James J., Jr., 132, 133, 134, 135, 138
McDevitt, William J., 170
McDivitt, James A., 85
McGratten, Robert, 73
MacInnis, Dr. Joseph B., 79, 80, 218
McKelvey, Dr. Vincent E., 17
Mackenzie, Kenneth V., 115, 213, 214
McLean, Dr. William B., 123-124
Magnesium from sea, 210
Magnuson, John J., 96
Malloy, Richard J., 158
Manganese, 16, 17, 140 ff, 156, 204, 205, 206
Manheim, Dr. Frank T., 17, 145, 147
Manson, D. Vincent, 33
Marianas Trench, 40, 94-95
Maritime Museum, 219
Markel, Art, 15, 44, 45, 46, 47, 49, 61, 159, 202, 203, 204, 205, 207, 208
  in H-bomb hunt, 169

Marlin
  black, 69
  blue, 59, 86
  striped, 59
Martha's Vineyard, 152
Mauna Kea, Hawaii, 117
Maury, Matthew Fontaine, 93, 132
Mavor, J. W., Jr., 64
Mechanical arm, 15, 19, 31, 34, 48, 55, 57, 88, 98, 113, 151
  in H-bomb recovery, 170
  recovery of, 89
Menzies, Dr. Robert J., 53, 62-65, 154, 157
Mero, Dr. John L., 17
Mesoscaphe, 98
Metals in Red Sea, 204-207
Meteor, 206
Meyers, Louis F., 173
Miami, University of, 18, 153, 156
Miami Seaquarium, 45, 97, 158, 215, 216
Microtektites, 194
Mid-Atlantic Ridge, 116 ff, 192, 193, 196
Mid-Oceanic Ridge, 117
Miller, Commander Mike, 86
Miller, Neil C., 173
Milliman, J. O., 146, 147
Milne, Lorus J., 37
Milne-Edwards Deep, 62-65, 154
Minard, Glenn, 21, 109
Minerals, 83, 156, 157, 203
  in Red Sea, 204-207
  from seawater, 210, 211
  see also Undersea mining

Minesweepers, in H-bomb hunt, 166
Missile, Sidewinder, 184
Mizar, 169, 170
Modlin, Carl J., 173
Monaco, Prince Albert of, 55
Monster
  Alexander the Great's, 120, 124
  Deepstar, 22, 57 ff
  Scripps, 59, 60
Moore, Donald C., 123
Moran Tugboat Company, 78
Morids, see Rattail fish
Morris, Christopher, 173
Morris, L. C., 49, 170
Mountaineering, undersea, 119 ff, 125 ff
Mountains, undersea, 116-118, 119, 125-130, 131-135, 192, 193, 196-198, 199, 217
  Arctic Ocean range, 193
  Mauna Kea, Hawaii, 117
  Mid-Atlantic Ridge, 116 ff, 192, 196
  Mid-Oceanic Ridge, 117
  see also Canyons, undersea; Cliffs, undersea; Seamounts; Volcanoes, undersea
Museum, underwater, 219
Myctophid, 137
Myctophid-like fish, 137

N

Narcondam Islands, 117
Natale, Robert R., 173

National Aquarium, 18
National Geographic Society, 37, 206, 210
News Bulletin, quoted, 210, 211
National Institute of Oceanography, Great Britain, 206
National Oceanographic Data Center, 152
National Science Foundation, 195, 204
Natural History, American Museum of, 33, 182
Nautilus (fictional), 43 ff, 64, 72, 75, 204, 205, 207
see also *20,000 Leagues Under the Sea*
Naval Civil Engineering Laboratory, 219
Naval Hydrographic Office, 132
Naval Oceanographic Office, 47 ff, 132, 139
in H-bomb hunt, 164, 167
Naval Ordnance Test Station (NOTS)
China Lake, 165, 184
Pasadena, 171
Naval Research, Office of, 85, 167, 180
Naval Research Reviews, quoted, 90, 170, 172
Naval Ship Research & Development Center, 119
Naval Undersea Warfare Center
Pasadena, 123
San Diego, 52, 115, 213
Naval Weapons Center, China Lake, 122, 165

Navy Atlantic Fleet Weapons Range, 49
Navy Deep Submergence Systems Project, 122, 175, 177-179
Navy Electronics Laboratory, 52, 101, 115, 136
Navy rescue, search, and recovery submarines, 100
Navy Underwater Sound Laboratory, 36
Navy Yard, Portsmouth, N.H., 34-35
Nekton, 149
Nenue, 97
New Providence Development Corporation of the Bahamas, 40
Newton, John, 156
Niagara Falls Aquarium, 39
Nicolson, Captain William M., 178-179
Nitze, Paul H., 46
Nodules, 16, 17, 83, 141, 145
Noise under sea, importance of, 95
Non-Existent Seamounts—A Case Study, 132
Norman, J. R., 58
Norris, Kenneth, 217, 218
North American Rockwell, 219
Ocean Systems Operation, 34
Northrop's Nortronics Division, 178
Notable, 166
NR-1, 35, 211, 212, 213
Nuclear power from seawater, 211

Nuclear reactions inside globe, 199
Nuclear-powered deep-diving boat, 35, 211, 212, 213
Nylon line, 171-172

O

Oarfish, 59
Ocean Bottom Search Sonar in H-bomb hunt, 162 ff
Ocean Science News, quoted, 168, 169
Ocean Science and Technology (pamphlet), 210
Ocean Systems, Incorporated, 76, 77, 217
in H-bomb hunt, 164, 167
Ocean Systems Operations, 34
Ocean Systems Organization, 25
Oceanauts, 35
Oceanic Foundation, 218
Oceanographer's Canyon, 88, 89
Oceanographic Data Center, National, 152
Oceanographic Institution, Woods Hole, 17, 31, 38, 54, 64, 85, 87, 88, 89, 93, 121, 134, 137, 138, 144, 146, 190, 204, 205, 206
Oceanographic Laboratories, Atlantic, 126
Oceanography, 219
definition of, 80
future of, 209-222
see also World records in oceanography

Oceanography, National Institute of, Great Britain, 206
Oceanography, Scripps Institution of, 31, 54, 59, 60, 96, 126, 150, 156, 219
Oceans of the World, 58
Octopus, 146, 186
deepest observed, 146
one-inch long, 195
Office of Naval Research, 85, 167, 180
Oil, 83, 154, 155, 192
Oil wells, offshore, 83, 217
see also Undersea mining
Open Sea, The, 37
Operation Deepscan, 196-197
Ophiuroid (brittle star), 22, 102, 113, 129, 146, 213
Ordnance Test Stations, Naval (NOTS), 165, 171, 184
Oregon City, 179

P

Pace, Robert, 171
Pachette, Arthur, 217
Pacific Ocean
plant and animal life in, 213, 214
size, 209, 210
Palomares, Spain, H-bomb hunt, 162 ff
Parhan, William B., 108
Parker, Barnie A., 173
Pasadena (Calif.)
Naval Ordnance Test Station, 171
Naval Undersea Warfare Center, 123

Penguins, 194
Pennsylvania, University of, Museum, 32
Pennsylvania State University, 122
Perchlike fish, 154
Peres, Jean, 197
Perry, John H., 31, 164
Perry Submarine Builders, Incorporated, 77
Peru-Chile Trench, 62 ff, 182
Petrel, 171, 173
Petroleum, 83, 154, 155, 192
Philadelphia Maritime Museum, 219
Philippine Archipelago, 128
Philippine Sea, 179
Phillips, Craig, 18
Phone, underwater, 23, 50, 112
Phosphate, 16, 17, 156
Phosphorite, 145
Physical Geography of the Sea, 93
Physonects, 137
Piccard, Auguste, 94, 101, 102
Piccard, Jacques, 71, 91-99, 101, 102, 203
Piccard, Marie-Claude, 99
Pilkey, Dr. Orrin, 156, 157
Pillsbury, 153
Pinnacle, 166
Pioneer, 117, 125 ff
    log of, 127, 128, 130
Pitman, Walter C., III, 198
Pitts, Captain Ray M., in H-bomb hunt, 164
Plankton, 18, 24, 51, 70, 71, 74, 88, 136, 146, 149, 154, 157, 187, 215

Plankton—*cont.*
    at great depths, 154
    observed from *Alvin*, 146
    observed from *Deep Quest*, 24
    observed from *Star II*, 70 ff
Polypropylene line, 170
Ponce de Leon, 92
Popular Science, quoted, 81
Porkfish, 158
Porpoise
    deepest dive of, 45
    noise of, 95
    training of, 217, 218
Portuguese man-of-war, 97-98
Potash, 156
Pratt, R. M., 141
Pressure at depths, 202
Prince William Sound, 159
Privateer, 48
Project Rock Site, 216
Pryor, Taylor A., 83, 218
Pryor, Mrs. Taylor A., 218
Pteropods, 144
Puerto Rico Trench, 197
PX-15, 91-99, 203

Q

Quarters, undersea, *see* Living on bottom of sea
Quinn, Edwin C., Jr., 170

R

Radio buoys, 177
Raft, nenue, 96, 97

Rainnie, William Ogg, Jr., 84, 87 ff
in H-bomb hunt, 167, 171
Ransone, Morris A., 173
Rasher, 100
Ratfish, 113
Rattail fish, 27, 142, 145, 195
Raymond, S. O., 121
RCA tubes, 171
Reave, William, 173
Rechnitzer, Dr. Andreas, 94, 101, 102
Red Sea explorations, 204-207
Red snappers, 145, 216
Researcher, 34
Rescue, search, and recovery submarines, 100, 175-180, 185
Revelle, Dr. Roger, 210
Reykjanes Plateau, 207
Reynolds, J. Louis, 46, 50
Reynolds International, Inc., 15, 31, 34, 169
Reynolds Metals Co., 203, 207
Reynolds Sub-Marine Services Corp., 170, 202
Ribbonfish, 59
Rice University, 190
Rift valleys, 193, 205
Rival, 166
Robert D. Conrad, 191
Robot, 59-60
CURV, 171 ff
FISH, 218, 219
side-looking sonar, 162 ff
Rockfish, 102, 186
Rodgers, Gene, 29, 30, 35, 36, 41

Rogers, Dick, 125-130
Roper, F. E., 213
Royal Geographic Society, 200
Rudderfish, 97, 98
Ruddiman, William, 155
Run Silent, Run Deep, 92
Rutherford, Alfred Lien (Al), 36-42, 49, 50, 51, 73

S

S-4, 179
S-51, 179
Sablefish, 54, 113, 214
Sachs, P. L., 121
Sailfish, 59, 86
St. Peter and St. Paul's Rocks, 117
Salt domes, 192
Salt from seawater, 210, 211
Salute, 166
San Clemente Escarpment, 185-188
San Clemente Island, 216
San Diego (Calif.), Naval Undersea Warfare Center, 52, 115, 213
San Diego Trough, 57
San Lucas Canyon, 150
Sand dollar, 129
Sand dunes on sea bottom, 159
Sandy Hook Marine Laboratories, 59
Saner, Don, 21, 25
Santa Catalina Island, 52
Sardine-like fish, 146
Satellite, navigation by, 190-191

Savonius rotor, 141
Sawfish, 58
Scallops, calico, 47, 203
Schick, George, 60
Schilling, John, 159
Schlee, John, 215
Schoffs, Gerald J., 173
Science, 137, 198
Scorpion, 179
Scorpion fish, 216
Scripps Canyon, 101-102, 151
Scripps Institution of Ocean-
    ography, 31, 54, 59, 60, 96,
    126, 150, 156, 219
  monster discovered, 59 ff
Scuba divers, 215
  in H-bomb hunt, 173
Sea, size and volume, 14, 209
Sea anemones, 39-40, 146, 183,
    214
  at great depths, 154
  Granny, pet, 40
Sea bottom, *see* Bottom of sea
Sea cucumbers, 22, 102, 129,
    145
  at great depths, 154
  lack of in lifeless depths, 53,
    54
Sea Diver, 79, 86
Sea fans, 118, 143, 183, 214
Sea lilies, 128-129, 143, 183, 214
Sea pens, 27
Sea plume, 186
Sea serpent, 41, 120, 124
Sea snail, 144
Sea snow, 70, 146-148
Sea spiders, 183
Sea urchin, 71, 113, 129, 186
Seahorse Shoal, 127, 130

Sealab II, 217
Sealab program, 217
Seals, leopard, 194
Seamounts, 125 ff, 131 ff, 192,
    217
  American Scout, 132 ff
  Caribbean, 134
  Cobb, 130, 217
  men reach summit, 125 ff
  off South Africa and New
    Jersey, 192
  vanishing, 132 ff
  Vema, 130
  see also Mountains, undersea
Search-and-recovery mission,
    record depth, 47-48
Seas, Maps, and Men, 63
Seasick machine, 217
Sediment, 47-48, 141, 142, 144,
    192
  Red Sea, 205, 206
  see also Bottom of sea
Serfass, Robert E., 46, 49
  in H-bomb hunt, 169, 170
Serpent star, 113
Sessions, Meredith, 60
Shark
  dogfish, 142, 146
  Greenland, 60, 61
  guitarfish, 186
  lack of in lifeless depths, 52
  large, 61
  leopard, and sea anemone, 39
  Mako, 145
  with ribbon-like tail, 102
  sleeper, 60
  thresher, 140
  unknown, off Hawaii, 61
  whale, 58

Shepard, Dr. Francis Parker, 96, 150, 151
Ship Research and Development Center, Naval, 119
Shisler, William D., 173
Shrimp, 18, 73, 137, 152, 161, 187, 218
  blue, 195
  deepest-dwelling, 95
  fish cleaners, 158
  Flammenwerfer, 94
  luminescent, 161
  red, 37, 95
  red and white, 46
  royal red, 18, 203
  two-foot long, 18
Shrimplike creature, 154
Shrimplike crustaceans, 147-148
Shumaker, Larry, 21-28, 100-103, 109
Sidewinder air-to-air missile, 184
Silas Bent, 135
Silver, 16, 204, 205, 207
Silvis, Robert M., 173
Simo-Orts, Francisco, 167
Siphonophores, 41, 137
  giant, 41, 42
Skate, 19, 97, 98
Skate, 18, 145
  deepest-dwelling, 20,000 feet, 197
Skipjack, 19
Slurp gun, 41-42, 114, 137
Smith, Admiral A. C. (Chet), 76, 81, 218
  in H-bomb hunt, 164
Smith, Dr. Gail P., 119

Smithsonian Institution, 213, 218
Snails, 145
Snappers, 33, 145, 216
Snow, sea, 70, 146-148
Solelike fish, 148
Somniosus microcephalus (Greenland shark), 60, 61
Sonar, 18, 23, 44, 50, 62, 63, 95, 137, 138, 147, 167
  high-resolution, 170
  locates schools of fish, 18
  side-looking, 162 ff
Soucoupe, see Cousteau; Diving saucer
South Africa, undersea mountain off coast, 118, 192
Southland, 133, 134
Southwest Research Institute, 104 ff, 122, 184
SP-300, see Diving saucer
Space flights, highlights of, 85
Spanish Sahara, 118
Specimen, 15
Sphalerite, 206
SPID (Submersible Portable Inflatable Dwelling), 78, 79, 80, 82
Spikefish, 30
Spiny urchins, 145
Spio fulginosus (worm), 56
Sponge, 79, 118, 142, 143, 195
  basket, 187
  glass, 182
  siliceous, 146
  tulip, 113
  TV-antenna-shaped, 196
Sputnik, 174
Squalus, 179

Squid, 54-55, 136, 137, 145, 187
  Atlantic Coast, 37
  fire, 153
  giant, 212
  giant vs. sperm whale, 212-213
  large, 18
  mating of, 213-214
  nerve fibers of, 153
  Star III attacked by, 36-37
  with white luminescent ink, 153
  with yellow ink, 147
Stachiw, Jaroslav P., 122
Standard Oil Company of New Jersey, 83
Star I, 30, 37, 69, 219
Star II, 30, 37, 66-74, 160, 161, 219
Star III, 29, 30, 31, 36, 37, 38, 40, 41, 219
Starfish, 27, 129, 146, 186, 214
  lack of in lifeless depths, 53
  new species, 195
Starlifter, airplane, 176
Steel
  high yield, 178
  maraging, 104, 108
Stenuit, Bob, 77-80, 82
Stephan, Rear Admiral E. C., 164
Sternoptyx, see hatchetfish
Stevens Institute, 207
Stewart, Dr. Harris B., Jr. 125-130
Stommel, Henry, 93
Strain-gauge readings, 28, 50, 51
Strasburg, Donald W., 33

Strategic Air Command, 165
Straza, 18
Stuart, Ray, 218
Sturgeon, ocean, 59
Submarine Development Group One, 179
Submarine disasters
  see F-4; S-4; S-51; Scorpion; Squalus; Thresher
Submarine valley, in Red Sea, 204
Submarines
  deep-diving, 13-14, 24
  deepest diving, 175-180
  dry-land testing, 104 ff
  log of, 140-144
  recovery, 179
  rescue, 175 ff, 185
  search, 179-180
  20,000-footers, 175-180
  wheels on, 15
Submersible Portable Inflatable Dwelling (SPID), 78, 79, 80, 82
Sub-porter, 108, 109
Sumatra, 117
Summers, Rear Admiral P. E. (Pete), 21, 22, 24, 27, 105, 108, 109
Sunfish, 58-59
Sunken cities, 63-65
Sunship Company, 34, 105
Surtsey, new volcanic island, 207
Swallow, J. C., 121, 206
Swallow floats, 93, 121
Swan Island, 128
Swanson, Rear Admiral L. V., 163

Swordfish
  Alvin attacked by, 89-90
  broadbill, 58

T

Tailliez, Commander Philippe, 102, 152
Talkington, Howard, 171
Tarpon, 59
Task Force 65, seeks H-bomb, 163 ff
Taylor, Glen, 217
Telephone, underwater, 23, 50, 112
Telephone cable, inspection of, 29, 30
Texas, University of, 58, 80
Texas Technological College, 47
Thomas Washington, 219
Thompson, Joe, 22, 57-59, 61, 110 ff
Thresher, 84, 102, 163, 166, 169, 174, 179
Timor, 117
Tin sands, 157
Titanium, 16, 178
Titov, Gherman S., 85
Tongue of the Ocean, 85 ff, 202, 215, 218
Torpedo Mark 46, 184
Tourist Observation and Underwater Research Submarine (TOURS), 219
Tracks on sea bottom, 195-196, 216
Transponder, 218

Transquest, 23, 25, 27, 109
Treasure ships, 207-208, 219
Trenches
  Aleutian, 193-194
  Kurile-Kamchatka, 154
  Marianas, 40, 94-95
  Puerto Rico, 197
Trieste I, 58, 84, 94, 100, 101, 102, 109, 123, 136, 137, 213, 214, 219
Trieste II, 101, 179, 180
Triggerfish, 97
Triton, 117
Trumbull, Jim, 88, 89
Tuna, 86
  bluefin, 59, 86
  skipjack, 32, 33, 211-212
Turbidity currents, 182, 194, 197
Turner, Ted A., 173
Turtles, 92
  green, 117
TV cameras, 97, 98, 203
  in search for H-bomb, 171
20,000 Leagues Under the Sea, 43 ff, 72, 73, 75, 90, 93, 96, 176, 189, 196, 201, 203-204, 205, 207, 209, 221

U

Ultraviolet light, 186
Undersea canyons, 88-89, 117, 150, 151, 183, 192, 197
Undersea cliffs, 32, 41, 88-89, 151, 155, 186, 216
Undersea habitats, 78 ff, 119, 204, 216, 217, 218, 219

Undersea mining, 83, 155, 156, 157, 210, 211, 217

Undersea mountaineering, *see* Mountaineering, undersea

Undersea mountains, *see* Mountains, undersea

Undersea Warfare Centers, Naval, 52, 115, 123, 213

Underwater museums, 219

Underwater Sound Laboratory, Navy, 36

Underwaterman, 220

Underwood, Robert, 173

UNESCO Conference, 152

UNESCO Courier, 210

Union Carbide Corporation, 164

United States Coast and Geodetic Survey, 17, 34, 83, 125, 133, 134, 158

United States Geological Survey, 16, 17, 88, 145, 152, 157, 205, 215

United States Navy, *see entries beginning* Naval *and* Navy

United States Sixth Fleet, seeks H-bomb, 163 ff

University of California, 54

University of Florida, 19, 46

University of Hawaii, 33

University of Miami, 18, 153, 156

University of Pennsylvania Museum, 32

University of Texas, 58, 80

University of Washington, 54, 217

Usry, Dick, 13, 14, 110-115, 137

V

Vema, 190, 191, 192, 195

Vema Seamount, 130

Verne, Jules, and *20,000 Leagues Under the Sea*, 43 ff, 72, 73, 75, 90, 93, 96, 176, 189, 196, 201, 203-204, 205, 207, 209, 221

Vetlesen Prize, 200

Vine, Allyn, 85, 197, 221

Virginia Polytechnic Institute, 141

Volcanic Island, Surtsey, 207

Volcanoes, undersea, 95, 118, 159, 192, 196, 199

see also Mountains, undersea

Voss, Gilbert L., 153

Vrai Histoire d'Alexandre, La, 120

W

Wacosta, 133, 134

Wahoo, 33

Wake Island, 193

Wakelin, Dr. James H., Jr., 218

Walford, Dr. Lionel A., 59

Wallen, I. E., 213

Walsh, Lieutenant Commander Don, 95, 100, 102

Washington, University of, 54, 117

ESSA research center, 217

Water, fresh, from sea bottom, 156

Weapons Center, Naval, 122, 165

Wendt, Gerald, 210
Wenzel, J. G., 106, 221
West Germany, *see* Germany, West
West Indies
  sea cucumbers in, 129
  sea fans in, 118-119
Western Geophysical Corporation, 165
Westinghouse Electric Corporation, 31, 34, 35, 53, 175
  in H-bomb hunt, 167, 173
Whale
  black, 212
  blue, 212
  and krill, 26
  noise of, 95
  returns echoes, 136
  sperm, 104, 212, 213
White, Edward H., 85
Willm, Pierre-Henri, 94, 102
Wilson, Valentine, 87, 89-90, 141, 145
  in H-bomb hunt, 167, 168, 172
Wittman, Walt, 97
Wolff, Dr. Torben, 154, 157
Wollin, Goesta, 199
Woods Hole Oceanographic Institution, 17, 31, 38, 54, 64, 85, 87, 88, 89, 93, 121, 134, 137, 138, 144, 146, 190, 204, 205, 206
  in H-bomb hunt, 167
Working lockout dive, deepest, 218
World's highest mountain (Mauna Kea), 117
World records in oceanography

World records—*Cont.*
  bathyscaphe dive, 94-95, 102
  deepest animals, 154
  deepest fish caught, 55
  deepest flatfish, 95
  deepest shrimp, 95
  deepest skate, 197
  dives by individuals, 78, 217 218
  geological specimen from sea, 15-16
  offshore oil wells, 83
  porpoise dive, 45
  research dive, 91
  rise of sea bottom, 158
  search and recovery mission, 47-48
  submarine dives, 21, 51, 84-88
  working lockout dive, 218
Worm tubes, 56, 148, 214
Worms, 27, 79, 146
  polychaete, 154, 183
Worthington, Robert K. R., 25
Worzel, J. Lamar, 191
Woy, Marshall E., 109

Y

Yakutat, 134
YFU 53, 185

Z

Zarudski, E. F. K., 89, 146
Zinc, 204, 205
Zooplankton, 146

ABOUT THE AUTHOR—

Gardner Soule was born in Texas, graduated from Rice Institute, and received his master's degree from Columbia. A former newspaperman, he has been a free-lance science writer for over fifteen years. He has written articles for many magazines and newspapers, including *Popular Science* and United Features Syndicate. His most recent book was *The Ocean Adventure: Science Explores the Depths of the Sea*, which was published in 1966, and he is also the author of seven science books for teen-agers. The Navy League awarded him a citation in recognition of his contribution to the field of oceanography. Mr. Soule is married and lives in New York City.

PRINTED IN THE U.S.A.